The Evacuee

or Sins and Comeuppances

The Evacuee

or Sins and Comeuppances

Ken Chadwick

Matador
9 Priory Business Park
Kibworth Beauchamp
Leicestershire LE8 0RX, UK
Tel: (+44) 116 279 2299
Fax: (+44) 116 279 2277
Email: books@troubador.co.uk
Web: www.troubador.co.uk/matador

ISBN 978-1780880-181

British Library Cataloguing in Publication Data.
A catalogue record for this book is available from the British Library.

Typeset in Aldine by Troubador Publishing Ltd, Leicester, UK
Printed and bound in the UK by Troubador Publishing Ltd, Padstow, Cornwall

Matador is an imprint of Troubador Publishing Ltd

MIX
Paper from
responsible sources
FSC® C013056

Thank You

Reading, advising, correcting, *encouraging*, all have been unselfishly volunteered by – in particular – Jenny Blant, Fiona Griffiths and Tina Cole. With other kind readers of drafts along the way, you sparked the book along. I needed that keen and highly valued interest.

The Evacuee thrived with your generous help. Thank you.

And thank you Janet: my lovely, loveable wife. Your regular advice is to 'Get on with it; just do it!' Well I have my love: here is the book (*and* the lawn is cut!).

Most of all – Thank you to Matthew, my son.

Ken Chadwick
Tenbury Wells. July 2012.

Chapter 1

Young Frank Bourne had never been so lonely, or so alone. He was in a crowd, one among more than three hundred school children herded onto the down-line platform of Birmingham Aston railway station. Three hundred children were meeting the war.

They had been gathering here throughout that early September morning in 1939. Arriving at the station mainly in groups, they were shepherded by teachers, though a few children, Frank noted were still with their mothers. Clearly these were very special children. They were clutched by mothers who could not be persuaded to leave them. Indeed throughout the morning, a few of these tight partnerships dissolved away altogether. They retraced their steps: to face war together, at home.

Bossing and fussing over the herd were twelve grown-ups – teachers, nuns and volunteer helpers – all trying to establish some order in this scene of much confusion, much of which was created by their own activity. For in a natural desire to rise in the pecking order of authority, each amateur crowd controller was tending to shout more loudly than the competition. Notwithstanding this they managed to marshal the predominately patient and mainly obedient herd into identifiable and countable groups. Herding and counting seemed to be the main point of the exercise, but keeping them safe was of high priority also.

"Get away – Get AWAY from the platform's edge!" Constantly the children were bombarded. The instruction was frequent, loud, and louder still. Perceived authority rested with the loudest voice.

Their work was having effect, and compartment sized groups were forming and dotting about the platform. Some groups were animated, well informed bodies of friends-together, bonded by religion, school or family. There were a few family groups, with the older child carrying, and displaying, the wearisome burden of newly imposed responsibility. One huddled group of street-wise children caught the eye: the nascent gang, already plotting.

Some younger children were crying, some in chorus, a few weeping alone. Many of the children were silent, alone within themselves in their allotted group, but most contributed to the blanketing noise. They reacted in varying degrees to the excitement of this so different day. The exciting difference dulled their aching for normality, and for home. They were being processed – being evacuated – being sent away. Sent away in confused hurry!

Frank Bourne, six – nearly seven – was standing on the fringe of one of the less noisy groups of children. He wanted to be invisible, but was cornered yet again, by yet another important grown-up. She turned him to face her while she checked the brown card label pinned to his misshapen, handed-down woollen jersey.

"Why are you standing with this lot?" she asked, loudly, but not unkindly. Without waiting for a reply, she found his details on her clipboard, studied the crowded railway platform, then steered him to another, quite similar gaggle of children.

"One of yours Miss Evans," she trilled, adding the quiet qualification, "I think." She pressed down firmly on Frank's shoulder, as though to affix him in this, his correctly allotted space, then she flurried off busy and important. Once again Frank eased himself to the fringe of his group. Eyes down, he wanted neither to be seen, nor even to see.

He found himself clutching a brown paper ration bag in one tight hand. Another important lady had passed them out to the children just now, promising, "They are very nice lunches." She warned against opening the bags before they were on the train – "Not even to look!"

'*Lunches*' sounded like food to Frank. As usual he was preoccupied by hunger but he did as he was told, he didn't look, but he allowed his fingers to explore the lumpy promises of the bag from the outside. The exploration made him hungrier still. With his other hand Frank clutched to his chest a brown paper parcel tied with well-knotted string: this was his '*Clothes for the War*'. The parcel wasn't heavy, but responsibility for its safety lay heavily on the six year old. More worrying still for the youngster was the need to guard the gas mask. Dire warnings from grown-ups had convinced him that without it he would die. The mask was in a cardboard box suspended on a string strap. The string cut into his shoulder. He rather wished that it was in a shiny leatherette case with a wide handsome strap, like several he could see. They were sported by some shiny looking children also part of the crowded railway platform scene.

The cardboard box though – with its strap of string – was a badge of his rank for, although he was unaware of it, Frank was in a uniform. He was wearing short grey trousers, wrinkled from a recent boiling; well-worn, too-big grey shirt; black rubber plimsoll pumps; limp collapsed stockings, and a scruffy, badly darned woollen jersey. The parcel of clothes; the stringed gas mask; his slight frame; lank hair; colourless complexion and his in-built deference, completed the uniform. It announced his status to all those who chose to care. Frank didn't care because he didn't know – but the world knew – he was from the slums.

The boy was the typical product of a typical Birmingham slum.

Home for Frank Bourne was a two-up, two-down house in a 'back-to-back' terrace of eight, exactly similar houses. The terrace stood parallel to a mirror row of houses ten yards to its front, while another similar terrace stood ten yards to its rear.

The areas to the front and rear of the houses were cobbled in part, but in the main they were topped with compacted earth and ashes. Some areas were tidy, some even showing signs of recent brushing. Many areas were littered, reflecting the disinterest, and even despair, lurking within its associated house. Refreshingly, but rarely, the last colour of limp and dying summer flowers showed where the occupants were younger: where they had not yet given up against the grind-you-down poverty. The flowers saying that hope, ambition and plans survived in this house.

None of the houses enjoyed in-house lavatory drainage, but a simple brick structure, at the top end of each court of sixteen houses served the communal needs. The structure housed two washhouses and four unpleasant water closets. Draughty, damp and odorous, the closets were lit only by the grace of ill-fitting and shortened wooden doors these permitted entry to daylight or moonlight, if strong enough. Some mornings Frank had to take the slops-bucket to the closet they shared with three other families. Inevitably the bucket was full to the weight that he could carry, and sometimes the night's pot-business needed two journeys. He hated the chore. Inevitably it made him gag. The heavy bucket was awkward to carry and it was painfully difficult to empty. However, being the youngest of the children meant that he did not get the hated job very often.

Helping in the washhouse was a more satisfying and regular job for him – but only monthly. It was hard work, but it was grown-up work. Although immediately adjacent to the closets the washhouse had much less stench. The large cast-iron boiler was built-in over a brickwork fire hearth. It was too high for him to lift up to, so when he had filled his bucket at the yard tap – to the level he could carry – and had lugged it to the washhouse, his mom took over and filled the boiler. She let him help her to arrange the newspaper, sticks and coal under the boiler and twice a month, on their allotted day for washing clothes, Frank was allowed to light the fire. Lighting the fire: that was good.

Things were happening so very quickly in the slow motion world of the boy as he stood, lonely and silent, on the railway platform.

4

He knew that there was going to be a war – a big fight – and he knew that he had to be here at the station because this was evacuation. He knew there had to be evacuation – so that Hitler could bomb Birmingham with his aeroplanes! He had neither heard nor understood everything that was discussed, but Frank had learned about evacuation when he had gone round to Mrs Smiths the other day. His mom had been summoned there, and unnoticed in the gravity of the occasion, his presence had been tolerated.

Mrs Smith was their immediate neighbour. She had a wireless set, and they currently enjoyed her goodwill. She was proud of her set, and importantly happy to share its benefit with them at this time. Luckily the accumulator that powered the wireless had been charged last week – at Evans, the hardware shop on the Lichfield Road. The aerial was in alignment, soil around the earth rod was freshly dampened, atmospheric conditions were good, and the temperamental instrument fed them news. News that added respectability to the facts they garnered from the main colourful source of their information. This was the neighbourhood bourse – the courtyard huddles, and gossip at the shops.

Last Thursday on the last day of August 1939, Mrs Smith sitting centrally before her polished wireless set had heard the terse Government command – 'Evacuate Now!' It was a shockingly immediate order. Importantly she had relayed it to Gladys Bourne. There was no time for Gladys to think or plan: Mrs Smith was holding court and Gladys was her captive audience. If you didn't pay attention to Mrs Smith – you didn't listen to her wireless.

"Everybody knew there'd be a war," she raged, "But they've done nothing... or nothing worth doing!" She thought for a moment, "I'll tell you what they've done... they've made lists! Oh yes and they've made coffins... our Lucy's Albert drives a lorry for the council and he's seen them... stacked up in this bloody great warehouse near Sutton... cheap and nasty... not proper coffins... not decent hardwood and brass handles. More cardboard than hardwood they are!"

More calmly she continued, "They've got to get the kids out... and clear the hospitals... and get them that's pregnant out of the city... or there'll be millions killed... I know it's breaking your heart Mrs Bourne, but your kids have got to go." She paused to marshal her argument, "The Eyeties have done it... Abbisinya! And you saw what happened in Spain. I tell you they're getting bigger and bigger... the planes – and the bleeding bombs!" Mrs Smith was well informed. Mr Smith had a job, and that allowed her to buy a daily newspaper and the luxury of time at home to read it. The newspaper and the wireless kept her bang up-to-date.

"The Germans started it. You saw the Zeppelins bombing us in the last bust-up. They'll do it again ... and it'll not be hundreds this time ... it'll be thousands killed ... thousands of raids and bombs ... and soon! We're all in the trenches this time ... it aint the place for kids! And they've left it too late – there's no time now to plan anything."

In any case Gladys Bourne was not a planner. She lived each day as it turned up: she survived each day. Survival was not a plan. Survival was an instinct.

This day was so different. Today Gladys had to get Frank ready and get him to the school, the school where he had started just a couple of days ago. At the school she would have to hand him over to somebody, probably some stranger and the stranger would get him away from Birmingham – to somewhere! It would be somewhere safe they said a place in the country. She took comfort in the knowledge that it would be a good and safe place in the country.

She had awoken this morning, alone with little Frank, and they were alone in an unusually quiet house. It was eerily quiet for his sisters, Rita and Jean, had left on their separate evacuation adventures yesterday. His mom had given Frank a 'proper wash', standing him in the sink and ignoring his squirming protests under the cold water. After the uncomfortable ablutions she had dressed him: darned but clean stockings, a washed and ironed grey shirt and pressed grey shorts – held up by repaired braces under the lumpy grey jersey. Who would help him to get dressed tomorrow? She worried over this as she prepared a breakfast treat for Frank: bread with margarine *and* a smear of gooey condensed milk, and sweet tea in a sparkling recycled jam jar.

She knew that Frank missed his sisters dreadfully. They were two and three years older than he was and naturally thus, his minders. They bullied him as a matter of course. They wiped his nose, and as necessary they had wiped his bottom. They dressed him, played with him when their jobs allowed, and they loved him, in the casual bossy manner of all sisters. Frank had pleaded to go with them on *their* evacuation, and tearfully demanded to know *why* he couldn't stay with them – but she had had to tell him that they must go by schools, and he had to go with St Josephs.

Frank's next older sister Joan, and his still older brother Charlie, lived with Granny Jenkins some streets away. Frank rarely saw them, or his gran. He wouldn't miss them. And especially he wouldn't miss Granny Jenkins. Appearing larger and angrier with every encounter, she frightened him. His Gran was always being angry with something or somebody. She 'took in washing' and was always trying to cope with the dreadfully hard work: impossible deadlines, impossibly dirty clothes, and clients whom she hated.

Frank would hardly remember Dave, his eldest brother, he too used to live with Gran, but he had left in the past month, and now, like uncle Charlie in the First War, Dave was in the Navy. Gladys thought that Frank *would* miss seeing Ellie, his eldest sister. She was married but still came round now and again – 'Just to row and fight with me,' thought Gladys. The visits always seemed to end with Ellie storming off, usually after noisy exchanges about her dad Bill.

Lord knows, but Bill had buggered off for good now. Frank had to work at remembering his dad, but Gladys guessed that he missed him.

Ellie missed him badly, and, although it was impossible to live with him, Gladys missed Bill as well.

Chapter 2

In the dull but dry September morning, Gladys Bourne held Frank's hand, as she shepherded her youngest child on the urgent walk to his new school, St Joseph's. She had briefly considered taking the tram – it could be free for evacuation day – but they were in good enough time and, just in case the tram wasn't free, they had walked.

She was glad that the September morning was without rain. It was dull of course – in and around Birmingham it was almost always dull. Thousands of tall factory chimneys and a million coal burning house fires fed the permanent mushroom pall domed above the industrial city. Winds, and perhaps a very good sun, were required before brightness could burn through to ground level. On the other hand a mild fog would immediately mate with the ever-present layering of smoke. It would thicken this into familiar, impenetrable, lung coating and deadly smog.

Gladys was not thinking of the weather conditions, beyond a mild satisfaction that the day being dry, had spared her one problem. Her unfashionable coat was worn, shabby and no protection at all from the rain and Frank was without a coat. She had considered letting him have Rita's coat – it was too small for Rita – but it was too big for Frank. The 'hand-me-down' reallocation of kid's clothing had petered out now.

Food came first. When you had bought food there was no money left for clothes. It was impossible for her to replace with new the clothing of the older children.

Mother and son made a forlorn pair as they hurried along the busy Lichfield Road. She carried the small parcel of his clothes, and she held his hand very firmly. She worried him about his brand-new and mysterious gas mask. "Look after it – don't drop it – or squash it. And don't lose it – you might need it. It could save your life." She instructed him further, "Always do as you're told. Don't talk unless you have to … you just listen!" She nagged on, "And don't you moan – ever."

The path to the Saint Joseph's school started along the exciting Lichfield Road, which was the spine of their neighbourhood. Fanning out at right angles from the long straight road were hundreds of courts, like their own, comprising thousands of back-to-back houses.

Along its route and on either side of it, hundreds of shops formed the road's frontage. Most had been converted from houses past. They were small with a single counter shop in the front and with living accommodation in the rooms above and behind this. They walked past an occasional double fronted shop, and now and then one or two houses that struggled to maintain their domestic identity.

The road was busy as always. There were competing grocers, fishmongers, and butchers – Gladys crossed the road, away from and well before Keats's – she had an overdue slate there. There were seed stores, greengrocers, bakers, pawnbrokers, fish and chip shops, and the Coop funeral parlour.

Two trams clattered past on rails built into the cobbled central area of the road. The driver of the outbound number 78 tram stamping on his foot bell clanged an acknowledgement to his colleague on the city bound 78. The din prompted a profane outburst from Mr O'Hare. He had been loading the flatbed horse-drawn cart in preparation for his greengrocery delivery round. Red-faced, he now ran from his shop swearing angrily and threateningly at the unnecessary and alarming din. His old horse though remained passive; he didn't appear to notice it. Outside the

9

newsagents a placard stand declared yesterday's news in large lettering, 'EVACUATION STARTS!'

Frank's mother spoke casually with a few people as they passed. To a friend of older acquaintance she recounted, "Rita and Jean have gone ... they were evacuated ... went yesterday ... Charlie and Joan are still staying with their gran ... that's until things settle down. ... So Frank is the last to be sorted out ... and here he is ... him off today." To another woman she had confided, "It does seem wrong – sending him off on his own at his age. I did ask if he could go with his sisters – they're very close – but the Council wouldn't have it – they have to go by schools!" You didn't argue with the Council. They didn't have time to alter a list. The tight lipped clerk had unnecessarily reminded her, "This is War, Mrs Bourne."

As they walked, and his mother talked to women she knew, Frank remained silent. He knew no one in this busy, noisy and crowded world. It was his nature to be silent.

They arrived at the bustling school and there, almost immediately, an identity label was pinned onto his chest. A second label followed, and then a third. As though to complete the parting ceremony Gladys handed a precious six-penny piece to her bemused son. With sudden sad surprise she noted how tiny her son was: a forlorn wee parcel of a boy.

He was handed to an unsmiling nun who told the choking Gladys Bourne kindly, but firmly, that it was time for her to leave.

For some time afterwards Frank recalled the cold hand on his cheek and the sad face of his mother as she turned away from him and left. More than three years would pass before they would see each other again.

Beginning the long walk home Gladys gathered her old coat tightly around her. She was returning to the silent and gloomy Pretoria Court: returning home alone – to number 3 back of 458 Lichfield Road. She walked with head lowered and with her eyes cast down. Oblivious to her familiar surroundings she walked automatically on the correct and shortest path home, and she experienced a great self-pity. Once again she was desperately unhappy: once again she was alone. It was another shit day – another miserable day in an unrelenting shitty life. She went deep into her misery, wallowing in the unfairness of it all, bemoaning the lack of a future, hungering for a success in her life.

Then suddenly she became aware that she was walking very, very slowly, almost standing still – there on the Lichfield Road pavement – and she became aware that she was crying: sobbing quietly. She looked up, searching for signs that her anguish, her crime of displaying despair, had been noticed. Straightening up, she choked back her tears, and resumed her normal gait.

Then she thought of the best time of her life. That was more than twenty years ago – when as a teenager in the First War she had earned good factory wages. She had operated lathes and capstans in that war, making munitions. Being important, feeling good, having friends, excitement, and happiness. She was walking more briskly now as she remembered that time: the time that had promised a future.

Gladys picked over the past twenty years of her life on that walk home from the school. Following the relief, the parties and the sheer joy of the Armistice she searched for other morsels of excitement in her life.

Meeting and marrying Bill had been a brilliant success in 1919, but she found few other bright spots. Following very quickly after the wedding, the birth of Ellie was another rare brightness. Again it was but a false success. And after the bright miracle of her first child, there had been – not joy – but pregnancies, and children, who had to be fed and clothed, and who had to share what little time there was left over for love of children.

The war had ended, it was a moment of glory, but her job, and with it her money, had ended with the war. The Armistice was to be followed by long jobless weeks, and jobless poverty.

Her husband was never to be completely well again. Bill returned from the War with a lung collapsed and made useless by the German bullet he met at Passchendaele. With but one labouring lung, he had little stamina to carry on his trade as a painter and decorator. The injury he carried sorely affected his strength, and his energy was sapped by the demands made by his breathing.

The promised future, the good-life implied by victory over the Huns, never materialised, and the wounded erstwhile hero became quickly disillusioned. He was just another soldier – returned damaged from the 'Great' war. Bill struggled with daily pain, the awful awareness of his one-lung vulnerability, and with the lingering trauma of his war experience.

Most of all he struggled with the hand-cart: a six foot flat wooden platform carried between two high, metal shod wooden wheels. He had to fight the cart daily, pushing it yard after punishing yard through the busy streets. He fought to balance its load. On most days this was dominated by the bitch of a cumbersome thirty foot wooden ladder. It was a continuous battle with the ups and downs of city roads: minefields of cobbles, and tramlines, and hustling, bustling people. All people concentrating on their own difficulties.

He had difficulty getting work and he had to go further and further afield to win it. A lot of the time doubting his ability to do it – and often anticipating the pain he was volunteering for – IF he won the job. Then, frequently the frustrating problem of getting paid for what he had done.

In the early years of their marriage Bill and Gladys had tried hard to build a home. Everything was possible then, indeed a happy future was not only possible, it was what they expected, and what they deserved. All was possible in the early flush of spontaneous lovemaking: love which was without fear and which brought relief and comfort to them both. But unremitting childbearing brought fear to their bed, and wrought unattractive body and mind changes. The lovemaking became increasingly less satisfying. At the same time, with less work, and less money to hand, the responsibility of building and maintaining a home became more and more difficult – and then it was impossible.

The marriage had stuttered through dismal poverty, made more acute by the six children who followed their first born Ellie. Now, after several short, but unexplained, and unapologetic absences, her man – her Bill – seemed to have gone forever.

War! In her life – of grey day following grey day – war was one more thing for Gladys to cope with. But there was a colour to war. Perhaps you were frightened, but you *could* win, and you knew that you *would* win. Not like the grey of this relentless poverty. You knew you could never beat this, you knew that you could never win.

Repeatedly she thought of her youth, remembering the blossoming factory days in the First War, recalling the friends, remembering the wages. There was always laughter: laughs about nothing, and everything. There was some flirting interest, mainly gossip and laughs; occasional excitements, and constant awareness that they were all part of a great common effort. Altogether the factory war had been a glorious time. NO! More than that! Something glorious – with wages!

Not for the first time in recent days Gladys allowed a secret thought into her head, a selfish pleasurable anticipation: she could go to work again.

Her factory experience during the First World War had given her specialist knowledge. She had worked lathes, operated presses and capstans. She had learned how to wrestle the bar feeds to heavy machines, how to adjust and maintain their critical settings, and how to speed work across them. She was confident that she retained the strength, and importantly the technique, for handling the heavy castings. She was certain-sure that she could still lug heavy shell cases onto machine beds, and she knew that she could still be a whiz on the presses and pillar drills. She knew how to work quickly and earn good money on the piecework system. She had forgotten nothing, and the machinery would not be so much different now than then.

Gladys tried to balance the excitement of these positive things spinning in her head with the awful reality of war. War was fear and danger. Again she saw her friend Lucy Atwood: blood spattered Lucy screaming and staring at the monstrous press that had consumed her careless hand. Again and unbidden she saw Jim ... what was his second name? Jim – his life blood crushed out of him – lying submerged under the toppled tons of heavy shell cases. They had collapsed at the slightest touch he had made in passing. She had seen people being hurt on the factory floor, had seen Jim killed, but she knew how to avoid these things. She knew that they were there, accidents waiting to happen.

The freezing winter mornings of the last time were not difficult to remember either. She had enough about her though; she was still able to shift her arse. Get up, have a cup of tea and a Woodbine. Probably that was the hardest bit, getting dressed in the cold dark house; fighting last evening's dead ashes in an uncooperative fire. Heating a kettle of water to soften her wash, and boil for tea. Then facing the walk to a repetitively hard factory day: probably swearing and cussing, but not complaining, never grumbling.

She began to enjoy the prospect now in her anticipation. She would work all hours available to her. She would be *involved* again. Earn money, and respect. She *could,* and she *would* have a life again.

It was entirely practical. Charlie and Joan already lived with their gran, and they would have to stay there. She would be able to pay something from her wages that would take the sting out of it for her mom. She could be without kids for a while now, and she would be. At forty years of age perhaps she could breathe again. With the little one gone today, there were no kids to stop her going to work again, and there was no husband to say no: she had no marriage that mattered.

Suddenly she experienced an exciting freedom. This war was

bringing changes. It offered a way out from today's miserable sameness. Through work and through wages it promised relief. Tomorrow she would go to Albrights in Rocky Lane. A board fixed to their factory gate announced, 'CAPSTAN OPERATORS WANTED' maybe, she debated; she should be at the factory before eight-thirty the next morning, to accept their invitation to 'Apply Within'. She would have to fight for that job. Many, if not most women living in Aston and Nechells were in the same boat that she was in. There would be a lot after the job, all of them desperate for a wage. She would have to be early. There was nothing remarkable about her and her need for a way out.

Then her determined optimism became a little less happy, smothered by a blanketing sense of guilt. She was a loser, and no longer did she have the strength or the capacity to be optimistic. She had given her kids away. People unknown were looking after her children. .Please God! Let them be good people ... people who have time in their lives for love; people who can afford the luxury of loving. Resisting this maudlin surrender to self-pity she made herself anticipate the next day of her life. HER life *could* be salvaged. With regular money she could be like other women. She could afford to love again.

She again forced herself to pick up the pace of her sad walk. The walk without option – the walk that was to the empty, cold and dark house that was her home. Her home alone.

Chapter 3

Early in the morning of the following day, as she had planned, Gladys Bourne was at the Albright factory gate in Rocky Lane. It was the first day without little Frank. Indeed it was the first morning in many years without any of her children able to dictate, to influence, or interfere with her plans for the day. Her very own day!

She missed them. Of course she missed them, however much she cherished her new found freedom. But her preoccupation with the important day ahead of her left her little time to mourn their absence. They all had a war to fight. Little Frank had to fight his little war at Roslington Village – but he would be happy there – Roslington was a nice and safe place in the country.

Expecting to find herself part of a crowd applying for work, Gladys was surprised and pleased to find that she was on her own. Getting there early had been a good idea. She was surprised because every family she knew was in sore need of wages, and factory jobs such as these were the only work that they could hope to do.

The gateman came from his wooden hut sited at the side of the entrance. He encouraged her with a smile and a cheerful greeting, "Hello my duck! You want personnel – I know you do!" Getting her smiling nod in return he went back into his tiny shed of an office, and telephoned for someone to collect her. The gateman looked familiar, and Gladys wondered if he had been at the factory during the Great War – but that was more than twenty years in the past! Waiting for her escort to arrive she plucked up courage to ask him. No he had not worked there then, he had been away at the war, but she would have seen him in the neighbourhood, he had lived in Aston all of his life. He volunteered that his name was Fred and he held out his hand. The blushing Gladys shook it and passed her own name to him. "Bloody Hell!" she thought, "two minutes into the place and I'm flirting already."

Feeling more cheerful and sure of herself, she raised a smile for the austere woman who arrived from the factory offices. She did not get a smile in return, and there was no conversation as she followed in the wake of this miserable looking, elderly office worker. Nothing has changed she mused. The man at the gate: he may have a different name, but he's still the same. He's OK. This miserable snooty cow from the front office is still the same. And I'm still the same: the same as I was twenty years back. Anybody meeting us – in the pub or in the market – would know that we were 'factory'. We have all got the factory look I suppose, me included. We all dress and look the part. Fred at the gate has got his flat cap and his smile on. Her, the bitch in front – in her two piece tweed suit – a smile would probably choke her. Then there's me, in a turban. Bloody hell if I'm not once again at the back!

Discovering that the division, the 'them' and 'us' divide, between shop-floor and front office, was still in place neither surprised nor depressed her. It was always thus.

It took very little time for Miss Hemming, the Personnel Officer, to record her details onto a small card: name, age, address, experience. She asked, "Have you had any experience Mrs Bourne?" The succinct response, "Haven't I ever had!" brought this part of the interview to a close, and Miss Hemming's eyebrows rising up into her fashionable fringe.

A cheeky faced lad of sixteen was called for. He took over at the personnel office and guided her across the yard and into the factory. She returned his cheeky grin with an instinctive wide smile and thought, "And I've seen you before as well my son!" The grin and the gob were the same. They were all of the same tribe, and as Gladys stepped into the factory she was on familiar, tribal home ground. The din, the bustle and the smells of oils and suds were exactly as she had left them in 1918. That was at the end of the war, more than twenty years earlier. It was twenty years ago when the work died, and the jobs dried up.

The foreman, in his polished brown boots, his stiff collar with navy blue tie, and his brown 'cow gown' was another 'familiar'. He was immediately interested that she had worked at the factory in the last war, and he took her on a tour of the work shop floors to show her the changes that he – mainly he – had made since that time. He was very proud of his kingdom, and Gladys could see why. The factory floor was clear and clean. White lines defined the various areas reserved for goods-in, raw materials, and castings. Work in progress; small parts stores, goods-out, all were identified and delineated. All these storages separated from the vibrant rows of machines: pillar drills, lathes and capstans likewise imprisoned within similar boundaries.

The two chatted for a while and Mr Brown's interest in her was an unusual reward in her day. He was impressed by her experience and enthusiasm. Her experience and obvious intelligence meant that little training was needed before she could once again operate one, or indeed any of the machines. He could start her on a capstan-lathe. It would be heavy work but she had convinced him that she could do it. She was keen to demonstrate that she was able to cope with that and any other of the intimidating machinery. When he had taken her to the capstans and lathes he had been delighted to discover that she understood and could perform machine setting: it was a time-saving bonus if an operator could step in when the proper machine-setter was busy. He had shown her the shell castings that, in probability she would be working on. With a four inch diameter base the casting weighed over sixty pounds. She would have to lift and lug these onto and off the lathe, with little respite throughout any eight hour shift.

Partly to impress him further, but more instinctively to find out if she still had the body strength and the required technique, she neatly manhandled a shell casting into the bed of the chuck bay. Impulsively she turned towards him, placed her hands on her hips and grinned in challenging satisfaction. He grinned back: surprised and pleased that she had done that without any suggestion from him. He told her so. He said that the factory expected to have to start day and night shifts shortly, when the expected orders built up, but to start with she would be on a straight day shift.

Mr Brown confided that management were surprised that at this early stage of the war the Ministry of Supply had not placed as many demands on them as they had expected. It appeared that top priority had been given to all things required by the Air Force, and that was why she had not met any competition for this particular job. Workers in the know were queuing at the motor factories, such as Austin and Morris for the higher paid work on offer there. These companies were changing a lot of production to airframes and aero engines, both in their existing factories and at the newly built 'Shadow' factories. Inevitably the Army and Navy would match the RAF priorities, and a great deal of their demands would fall onto the other Birmingham businesses – this Albright factory would get a lot of the business.

This unexpected lull before full production was good news for Gladys. She would have time to get settled in; time in which to hone her machining skills and get back her work-speed, ahead of the demand which would bring with it lucrative piecework. Anyway it would be difficult for her to get to the better paid aircraft jobs at Longbridge, or Castle Bromwich every day. What's more she didn't know about aeroplanes. She knew all about shells and she knew that she was a bloody good shell machinist.

"Oh my God!" she thought as she made her way to the factory exit, "Flirting at the main gate, and now I'm thinking of putting my name down on *this* bloke's dance list." But Mr Brown was *nice*: a gentleman – and liking him was not like getting into bed with him.

Anyway she had to like him: she had wanted this job. And she had got it! He had just told her that he wanted her to start the next morning.

Then, on the walk home, reality hit her. With remarkable clarity she remembered little Frank's white, dismayed face when she had left him, only yesterday, at the school. She had had very little rest through the night, his trusting face waking her whenever she drifted into sleep. Frank was the leading obstacle to her rest. She had to apply herself to thinking of all the others.

God Almighty – Jean and Rita are out there as well – staying with strangers. Jean was grown-up at eleven, but Rita's only a mite, not that much older than Frank. She consoled herself with the thought that Jean and Rita were together. She had made that clear to the nun who took charge of them at the school – was it only two days ago? She had made it clear that they could not be separated, wherever they were billeted. They would be alright together. But where are they? And where is little Frank?

Poor Frank, he is the baby and he's on his own! She consoled herself with the thought that Kids were the greatest survivors in the World. She had first-hand knowledge of how they coped with everything thrown at them. Everything was normal to kids of that age. They had no experience of anything else, and so, with everything normal nothing was unfair. She thought of her other children. They were all scattered about, they hardly knew her as their Mom. Once again she felt the guilt – the guilt that always arrived – that always came with any little satisfaction or happiness that chanced her way.

She thought about the day's happenings: the people she had met, particularly the men and for the first time she allowed herself to worry about the work she would be starting in a few hours. Then she thought about the future ahead. She had not grown soft living in Pretoria Court. With just a bit of training, some regular proper food and no kids to dictate her day to her, she was bloody sure that she could do anything required of her at that factory. She could even look forward to the work: the work which would bring challenges for sure, but which would come also with the excitement of new friends.

She looked forward to the payday even more so. She would be on a flat rate of pay to begin with, but as soon as the expected orders started to flow in she knew that she would be on piecework. Piece work was what she wanted – being paid for each item that she completed – it would add up to good money. Money had been missing in her life for more than twenty years. Money was food and clothes and coal: more than that – it added up to worthwhile life itself – and with it came respect. Respect was a rarity to be cherished – by someone not accustomed to a great deal of it.

Leaving Albrights with the job secured, Gladys deliberated for a while before making her way to the Nechell's Public Baths. She hired a towel, bought a small bar of yellow soap, and luxuriated in a hot deep bath for nearly an hour. She loved a good bath. It was sixpence well spent.

She slept more soundly that night than she had for more than a year. The images of her day lulled her to sleep: they merged with the images of the future that she could begin to see, and which she struggled to retain. The faces of Jean, Rita and Little Frank fogged out, and she was asleep without identifying the shadows on the edge of her consciousness. Perhaps that was Joan and Charlie at their gran's, and was that Dave in his uniform? Submerged under the day's happenings the misery ache was tolerable tonight.

Thoughts of Ellie hardly interfered with her deep sleep.

21

Chapter 4

Frank was confused, uncomfortable and rather frightened. Most of the children waiting on the platform with him were similarly discomforted. Going to the country was taking too long. They did not *want to go* to the country. It was a waste of time. The endless waiting reinforced the futility.

At long last something happened. Their train arrived. The dramatic size, smell and sound of the arriving steam engine: its weight and power moving the platform under their feet, terrified some of the all-alone younger children. Their weeping – for the normality that had abandoned them – became a screaming wide eyed urgency for someone to turn to: to hold on to. For most of the marshalled children however, it was an intoxicating end to the long, long boring wait that they had endured. They cheered.

Miss Evans, the last appointed guardian of Frank, frantically skipped and hopped along the front of her allotted part of the platform. "Stay – just where you are!" she screamed at her charges. "Come back here!" She yelled at the boys who had broken away, gathering to admire the great belching steam engine. Then, remembering the name of one particular breakaway miscreant, she screamed "Joseph Dunn! Come back here, immediately!"

Frank had remained obediently in his place. His melancholy, the disinterest of the past hours, had been shocked awry by the train's arrival. Quickly recovering his composure he edged towards the action. Impressed with the close-up train and the activity all around him, he grinned to see Joseph Dunne sauntering back to the group. He joined him. Joe was clearly satisfied with his inspection of the engine and its heroic captain. The engine driver, by returning Joe's thumbs-up greeting and salutation, had also passed muster.

The teachers travelling with them were dismayed to see that there was not a through corridor on the train. They could not supervise every self-contained compartment, there were not enough teachers. They could foresee inevitable problems and accidents. All they could do in prudent anticipation was to usher their charges through the platform lavatories – whether they wanted to go or not. They shared "Told you so!" shrugs with their colleagues when inevitably – as the compartment doors of the train were opened – there was a joyous free-for-all. The jostling and noise were particularly noticeable in the areas where grown-ups were thin on the ground.

Frank, forgetting about his home sickness, got stuck in and won a window seat. Immediately the doors were slammed shut however, there was a readjustment of the seating arrangement. An uncompromising, larger boy loomed over Frank: he met Joe Dunn.

Joe was a ginger headed eight year old winner. He had the slight frame common to children from the slums of Nechells. Unbowed though by his daily experience in the rough and tough industrial area of the city, his eyes were bright. He wore the uniform: grey shorts, scruffy jersey, rubber plimsolls, and a suspect neck. The string of his gas mask box was rebelliously tied around his waist. His crumpled, and by now tiny, lunch bag was stuffed into the box. Very little remained of 'the very nice lunch', the bag had been plundered long ago.

With an unambiguous nod of his head, Joe indicated where Frank *could* sit. Frank, thus directed, surrendered his hard-won window, and sat in the opposite seat. Having won his prime position, the new incumbent turned to Frank. "Have to sit facing the engine," he explained, with the clear implication that this was vital for the safe operation of the train. "What's your name nipper? What's your school?" Frank informed him seriously that he was Frank, he went to Saint Joseph's and volunteered that he was six, but nearly seven, adding, "I don't mind not sitting where you are – by that window – this window's OK." Joe laughed, "Good for you Frank – mate!"

The friendship was cemented when Joe gave him one of two comics he pulled from his stuffed jersey. "I don't know Saint Joseph's, but its Catholic ain't it, like mine, Trinity?" He introduced himself, "I'm Joe and I'm nine," and then added, "Well … nearly nine." He continued, "Call me Joe! *Don't* call me Ginger! And we can be mates like, we'll be friends." Frank liked that promise, and on Joe's instruction, without hesitation, he opened his paper ration-bag. "Shove that bar of choclit up your jumper Mate!" ordered Joe, "Sister bleeding Alice will be along … mark my words. The ugly black cow will have the choclit away." The chocolate was stuffed into his waist band, and only just in time.

The compartment door opened and the unmistakeable, fearful frame of Sister Alice filled the doorway. Holding out her hands towards them, she demanded that they open their bags. "These will be eaten at the proper time," she said, removing the chocolate bars from the bags which were opened in turn by the reluctant children. She stowed them away; magicking them into some hidden pocket within her huge black gown.

"Where is the chocolate, Dunn?" she grated after looking in Joe's almost empty bag. "Well … Sister Alice … I had it … then I was starving hungry … and I ate it … Shouldn't I ate it Sister Alice?" She glared at him and spat, "We will talk later Master Dunn!" Moving to Frank she looked in his bag, and menacingly she accused him, "So you've eaten yours as well!" He returned her stare without blinking. Wide eyed he slowly shook his head.

He was saved by the sound of a whistle and the noise of slamming doors. The nun read one of Frank's labels. "You and I will speak again," she threatened. "I promise you that we will get to know each other. In the meantime let me advise you, you miserable little tyke, if you listen to, or get involved with that heathen, Joseph Dunn here, you will get into more trouble than you know exists … and you will stay in that trouble! For the sake of your undeserving soul I would put you in another carriage. Unfortunately there is not time to do that – but be warned!" Pulling the door closed she left the compartment, as she slammed the door she looked directly and threateningly at Joe and Frank. She had no need to say a word more.

With the lingering effect of the nun's visit, the full compartment remained silent and fearful. Until that is Joe broke the silence with a raucous laugh when the bewildered Frank asked him, "What did she say … what's she mean?"

At last, another whistle was blown, and the train jerked into life. With no one now to forbid or control them, the children attacked the brown paper bags. Jam sandwich, currant bun, two round biscuits, an apple and an interesting banana. It was the first banana in Frank's life … and the last one he would have for several years. Joe and Frank giggled as they recovered their chocolate bars. Joe's bar already part eaten: the serrated edge showing the marks of his front teeth, where he had been nibbling. "I've been making it last … but shall us give the poor starving orphans a bit each?" asked Joe, already breaking his treasure and passing squares of chocolate to his neighbours, nodding towards others and instructing Frank, "You look after them others!"

Food kept the children relatively quiet for a time as the train alternately thundered, faltered and jerked them away into a new life. The children concentrated on the food bags. They became noisier as, according to taste, they swapped bits and pieces of their surprise packets.

Two tearstained infants, younger than Frank, were perched together. Oblivious to the noisy bargaining going on around them they were united in silent misery. Without interest they looked through the imprisoning windows at the passing town and countryside. The pair had been particularly betrayed by the brutal loss of the warmth and security of love. Betty Frome, at twelve the eldest of the twelve children there, spoke quietly to the pair. "There-there, never mind now – you'll be in the country soon – it'll be fun!" There was no response other than large distrustful eyes. She sat between them, and wrapping her arms round their shoulders, she lied, "You'll be seeing your mom soon." They clung to her and started crying once more.

Joe spoke to the infants to ask, "Don't you want them sand wedges – ain't you going to eat em?" Getting shakes of the little heads in reply; the sandwiches disappeared.

Following the luxury of the unsupervised, no-rules paper bag feast, the train journey soon became a routine in which fields; cows and buildings passed; then reappeared, and then passed again. Joe enlivened things when he leapt to his feet. "Let's have some fresh air," he shouted. He grabbed, pulled, and then released the broad leather strap securing the window, allowing this to drop with an uncontrolled, very satisfying thud. His companions were startled but they took their turns at the open window when Joe invited them, one at a time, to join him. They leaned out to better enjoy the speed, noise and smoke of the labouring engine, and they exchanged waves and shouts with other fortunate kids – lucky enough to be like they were – not trapped in supervised compartments.

Joe could not sit quietly while there was a challenge on offer. The overhead luggage rack was just such a challenge. It took the combined efforts of most in the compartment to complete the task. But under his shouted instructions, coaxing and bullying, it was finally achieved: he was manhandled, up and on to the netting of the rack. The turning moment of the exercise came with the hesitant intervention of Betty Frome. She volunteered her shoulders to Joe, and when she stood smartly erect the floundering lad was shot onto his target. They all screamed with triumph,

26

laughter, and with some relief. Joe lay back on the netting and milked the moment, stretching out, eyes closed, and with arms behind his head.

Frank was very impressed with the bravery and initiative of Joe. Sensing this, his hero cemented the new friendship by attempting to hoist his small frame up alongside him. His pleas for Betty's help were ignored however, and Frank couldn't quite make it without her tall help. Anyway Joe quickly became bored with the not so comfortable elevation. He tumbled down and resumed his reserved place by the open window, allowing Frank to stand with him for most of the time.

The journey extended into, and then beyond, a second hour. The train was an upstart: it had no status in the railway's planning, and hence it gave way to the established traffic: the legitimate trains of the great time table. It stopped inexplicably in open countryside; it thundered through uncaring stations, then infuriatingly, with no apparent reason it would stop again. The children knowing only that the distance between them and home was enormous; that it was getting greater, becoming impossible. The blasé acceptance of the stronger children became a little nervous; the tears of infants altered – first to silent sobs, and then to silent dread of the anticipated unknown.

Frank stayed within himself. He was neither particularly happy, nor desperately miserable, as he stood with Joe by the open window: even this thrill dulling into merely an interesting routine. He was in the cocooned state of unquestioning acceptance: the bubble that protects the inexperienced child from fearful anticipation of events. He thought not of days past – nor of days to come: they were just days. But he *was* happy to be with Joe – his Friend. He would never call him Ginger.

Chapter 5

The children's arrival and processing at Burton station was as confused as departure had been from Birmingham. However the evacuees were subdued and rather less noisy as they spilled out onto the platform. Weary, and some with faces reddened and blackened from open-window smoke and wind, the children were resigned as they submitted to yet another bossing-about.

"Line up by schools!" screamed a bully of a woman, sweeping her arms to indicate, "Saint Joseph's over here ... then Holy Rosary ... Sacred Heart ...Trinity towards the other end of the platform." She paused in mock despair, before calling in frustration to the several placard holders. "Please, *please* ... hold the school name cards higher ... and get your school parties together as quickly as possible. This is urgent! More trains are coming here"

She had been able to ignore a girl's tiny raised arm, but the initiative of the little girl's other arm wrapping round her leg compelled her attention. "Just get to your school group my dear." She looked at the infant's lapel label, "Look, there's your school Holy Rosary, over there. See the lady there first ... *then* you can go to the closet." She corrected herself, "... the lavatory."

Once again lists were consulted, registers were read, and the youngsters were coaxed and manhandled into appropriate bunches and lines. Frank tried to stay with Joe, but a 'no arguments' push by a supervisor propelled him into the St Joseph's group. Eighteen children between six and twelve years old formed that party. Frank was the youngest.

"Teachers and Guardians *please* take charge. Count them against your list and *keep them in line!*" This last accompanied by a frantic arm indicating a thumb sucking four-year-old casually escaping with her small teddy bear and gas mask. "One supervisor from each group please go to the waiting room," the large woman continued, "the RTO, the Transport Officer there will give you bus allocations for your group." Looking down and responding to an anxious plea from a young girl, who was holding her younger brother's hand, she continued, "Yes Dear ... I know you want to stay with George ... and we will *try* to keep brothers and sisters together," ... she finished lamely, "but..."

Eventually they were knitted into crocodiles, and clacked through the station and into the waiting single deck buses. Frank was thrilled to see Joe bundle himself onto the same coach. Although officialdom stopped him sitting by his new friend, the sight of him was a comfort. Clearly they were destined for the same village. Less comforting was the sight of Sister Alice, standing next to the seated driver – but Frank was sure now that evacuation – whatever it was – would be all right – with Joe.

By the time the coach reached the village of Roslington all on the bus were very aware of Sister Alice's presence. The heavily built, middle aged nun had sat, in her intimidating gown and headdress, starched and upright, in the front seat of the bus. During the forty-minute trip, with economy of gesture and movement, without shouting – and without question – she exercised absolute authority. "I am Sister Alice," she had declared, after the door had been closed on the filled bus at the railway station. "You will do as I say – of course – and always." Her voice was a harsh monotone; her eyes cold and bright in a set, expressionless face. Her head turned neither left nor right as she faced down the bus. Frank knew that she had seen him. He was scared: she didn't like him! "You will now sit quietly and properly. You will not slouch." She paused, "Trinity know me: Saint Joseph's – very quickly – *will* know me." Her presence was menacingly overpowering. The children were silent. She repeated, "I am Sister Alice," then turned away from them, and the driver had immediately obeyed her curt nodded order to take the vehicle, with its unnaturally quiet load of children, to their destination.

They motored via minor roads and tall-hedged lanes to the small Staffordshire village of Roslington. The place appeared to be asleep as they arrived in the late afternoon autumn sun. The bus trundled through the village on its way to the village hall. It passed the landmark Cherry Tree Pub. The Post Office was alone in showing a busyness of people seen through its open door. The children noted that the Post Office was also the shop. Later they found it to be a general store: selling groceries, haberdashery, tobacco, sweets, paraffin – and any and everything else called for by the villagers. A few cottages, many of their pretty gardens still busy with flowers and vegetables, filled the road frontage between the pub and the shop. Over decades, perhaps centuries, the houses and businesses had all been built on one long side of the roughly rectangular open green.

On the opposite side of the green, behind a gated stone wall, stood Roslington Church, and next to it the Church of England rectory. Fronting the further short side of the green was the village hall, sitting comfortably in its own grass paddock. The hall and paddock were fronted by the road, on the edge of which sat the War Memorial. It was a simple stone cross. The dozen or more names carved into its plinth were *'the sons of this village, who valiantly gave all in the Great War. Remember their glorious supreme sacrifice'*

The bus came to a stop here. They had arrived. The children quietly disembarked at the unspoken, gestured command from Sister Alice, who then barked, "Trinity – in line – here! Saint Joseph – stand in line here!" Once again they stood, silently, in Sister Alice-lines. They knew neither where they were, nor what would happen next, but they were nervously aware that they were now evacuated.

Father Daniel, Priest of Holy Trinity Church and the school's head teacher in Birmingham, was waiting in the village hall for the new arrivals. He came out to greet them, and the children were instantly relieved to see that he smiled. He smiled, and then he laughed, thigh-slapping loud for the children to hear. He laughed because he saw their need for him to laugh. He recognised the sadness, the apprehension and the sense of betrayal in them. Father Daniel forced himself to laugh.

The priest had not found it easy to laugh at all during the last few days. First the chaos in the Birmingham schools: arranging the evacuation of his own school and merging this with children from St Joseph's. Talking with distraught parents, trying to comfort them, but unable to give anything other than general assurance that all would be well. He had been chastened by the enormity of the task and the lack of precedent in dealing with it. He understood the stifling heartache of parents enduring the trauma of sending loved children into the unknown. But the greater heartache and misgivings came to him when, after running them to ground he talked with the other parents, the uncaring ones. They did not see the taking-away of their children as a problem. "Do what you like." … "Will it cost anything?" Above all he was aware of, and he feared the vulnerability of the children now in his care. His children.

The lack of organisation and goodwill that Father Daniel found in Roslington had been an awful start to this very long day. Arriving early he had looked for the only contact that he had been given, and at last he found him. The Reverend Humphries was dead-heading flowers in a hidden-away part of his very large garden, and clearly he was annoyed to have been discovered in this garden sanctum. "Evacuation? I have nothing to do with it Father," was his reaction to Father Daniel's introduction. "Church of England," he intoned deliberately. "My flock are C of E. – I understand that all of the *Evacuees,*" adding the grit of distaste to the word, "are of your different belief." He continued, "War or not I think that the entire matter has been badly managed – not thought out properly. This village is C of E; it is *not* of Rome. And now," he paused, to control his obvious annoyance before stating, "and *now* we are to have some thirty – *thirty* – *youths from the city* visited upon us. That's nearly as many children as our own – our own protestant children."

Father Daniels chose not to challenge the images of imminent crime, rape and head lice implied by the threatened *youths from the city* visitation. He had interrupted the Reverend's flow. "Regardless of creed, Vicar, children are children, and I'm sure that you and I have the same purpose in this. We have the urgent job of getting them housed. Let's get them *safely* housed. And then, at some better time in the future, perhaps you and I can debate the subtle differences of our dogmas." The vicar, with no intention of ever voluntarily speaking again with the Catholic priest, had repeated that evacuation was nothing to do with him. With little grace he directed him to the village police house, and impatiently he told him also where he was likely to find Mrs Hinton of the Women's Voluntary Service. Father Daniels filed him away in his mind, sinfully labelling him as the Reverend Pontius Humphries.

The Priest had been somewhat refreshed in spirit when thankfully he met Mrs Hinton of the WVS. She had been waiting on his arrival and was clearly pleased and relieved to see him. Explaining the preparatory work they had done, she walked with him to meet the local policeman Constable Round. Both were capable and energetic people who had been appointed by the local Council as Evacuation Reception Officers. They were the only people in any small way prepared for the coming emergency. Hopelessly ill equipped, they were aware that this influx would double the child population of the village.

The immediate brief was to match the list of arriving children with the register of available rooms. In the two days since the evacuation order had been given they found that this list of promised accommodation was hopelessly out of date. It had been compiled some hot months earlier, when the possibility of another war had been unthinkable. In a climate of optimistic peace, and the goodwill of *it will never be allowed to happen, anyway*, the local population had been magnanimous in their charity. *Now it had happened*, and the goodwill, and with it the offered accommodation, had shrunk; only the 'List: of children to be housed' was up to date.

Now that homes were actually to be invaded – occupied by kids from the city – it was found that many of the rooms, so generously offered months earlier, were no longer available. *'We have to look after our own – and our sick aunt is coming from the city to stay.' 'The room's needed now for a farm office.' 'The doctor says I'm not up to having another kid in the house.' 'Young Prudence is having nightmares about it.'*

Constable Round and Mrs Hinton rewrote the list, and between them they visited all of the prospective host houses. They fielded all of the objections, and they found support, and negation for most of the objections, in the Emergency Regulations. They arranged for loan beds; suggested an alternative place for the seed potatoes, other than the floor of the proposed evacuee room, and found that offering to send in willing neighbours to help clean the room was a most certain way of getting it cleaned – and without neighbourly assistance. The Emergency Regulations gave them authority to commandeer accommodation. But, "God help the poor little bugger going there!" Bob Round thought as the pair 'signed-up' and left another enforced, unwilling host. "That's a cold welcome for the duration," he confided to the subdued Mary Hinton.

Chapter 6

Father Daniel retained the laughing face with which he had greeted the party on their arrival at the village hall, and his voice was loud and happy when he addressed the nun. "Well that was very efficiently done Sister Alice. You have hardly been away at all, and now you are back, and with you … all these brave children."

More quietly, in a soft Irish brogue, he addressed the silent lines of bemused evacuees. "Hello children," he said. His greeting raised no response; he raised his arms in pantomime mock surprise that they had disappeared, and then he jovially repeated, "Hello children. And bless you, every one." Unhurriedly he continued, "And a big welcome to this lovely village, which is called ROSLINGTON." He paused as he looked up and down the lines, giving little hand and smile acknowledgements to those children whom he knew. "To those of you who don't know me," he continued, "I am Father Daniels." He confided quietly, "Now … as a penance for sins long ago committed, and long ago forgotten … by me … I am your teacher."

Then he invited them to mutiny, to break ranks, for he waved them towards the open door of the hall. "Let's have you all inside," he yelled, "there's pop and cakes inside." Some of them looked towards the starched nun. He paused, "What are you waiting for? … Don't you like iced buns?" When he invitingly pointed again at the open door the dam gave way and there was an unruly noisy surge into the hall. His laugh was genuine as he followed them in, appearing not to notice the rigid disapproval that was so evident in

34

Sister Alice's expression and rigid body. He laughed again, and the children loved him, already.

Frank felt a new confidence; he sought Joe on the scramble into the hall. They foraged together.

The hard work of PC Round and Mrs Hinton was further reflected in the turn out at the hall. It was crowded, and not all of the people, standing and sitting in groups, were unhappy at the prospect ahead. Everybody keenly studied the children as they were ushered into the hall by Father Daniel.

Sandwiches, buns, cakes, milk, water and lemonade were tidily, and even stylishly, laid-out on trestle tables set up along one wall. The Priest with an open handed sweep of his arms indicated the food, and without reserve the children attacked the arrangement. The symmetry of the table top food display was quickly destroyed by the children's frontal assault. The villagers saw the rapid break down of the pretty presentation. It was almost instantly transformed into untidy piles of food and then remnants of piles, before these too disappeared. Mrs Hinton and her ladies of the WVS were not dismayed, they were delighted at the success of their work. At a more normal WVS meeting they would judge and declare which was the *best* homemade scone. Here there was not a good, bad, or indifferent scone to be found for judging.

Father Daniel imperceptibly checked Sister Alice as she inclined forward, intending to impose order. The villagers watched in near silence as, very quickly, the nicely presented and plentiful food was demolished. Only the red apples remained to be devoured. Sister Alice, indefatigable, had by now positioned her black-garmented looming presence at the tables. Deliberately she selected and handed one red apple to each of the children. One by one the children accepted them, most held them uneaten for a long time.

Mrs Hinton, who had been talking with Father Daniel, smacked her clipboard to attract attention, "Quiet now please. Children will you please sit down – yes, on the floor – and we will get on with the allocation. Have your cases and parcels and gas masks with you when you sit down." She spoke quietly but with authority. The chattering subsided, and she then turned to Father Daniels inviting him to speak.

"Quietly now children," he said, "and quickly please, or we'll have it dark." He addressed the expressionless nun, "Sister, can you please arrange that all of the children face this way – they can sit in rows, perhaps a few feet apart – so that they can be spoken to individually – if need be." He waited for the predictable bustle to erupt. It did but, with Sister Alice standing in close proximity, the childish chatter and upheaval quickly and quietly subsided.

Frank had kept his nerve, and when the jostling eased and the lines of children were settled, the cross-legged boy was sitting next to the sprawled out Joe.

Father Daniel immediately commanded an attentive silence when he addressed them. "Children from Saint Joseph's, and children from Trinity, well done, all of you! You have had a difficult day – it has been a very different day for all of you – and you have all done really well. I am proud of you. Well done again. Now – now, you are going to meet new people: generous and kind people." He was looking down as he spoke, "They will be taking care of you." He paused before continuing, "They, and this village, will be your new home for a while. Just for a while! We all pray that it will be a very short time."

Many of the villagers present appeared distracted, and few of the children listened further as they digested this information. The Father explained the proposed school arrangements. He told them that the village hall that they were sitting in was to be their new school. It would become the local catholic school – serving not Roslington alone – but the surrounding villages also: all catholic children in the area would be taught here.

The intention was to open the school in a fortnight's time, on that September Monday. There was little time to organise furniture and school materials, but he would be there, with Sister Alice and hopefully another Sister, at nine o'clock on that Monday: prepared to start school, and to provide some continuity in the young lives. "Could the kind hosts arrange for the children to be there at that time, on that day?"

As he finished Father Daniel looked quizzically at Sister Alice. She accepted this as an invitation to speak and in her harsh monotone she laid down rules for the wide-eyed children: "There is no place here for unruly … dirty … disobedient ruffians. You will be obedient; do what you are told to do: when you are told. You will be clean. Speak when you are spoken to. You know, or you *will* know … your catechism, use your rosary, and be good Catholics." She looked directly at villagers around the hall as she continued, "Any complaint about behaviour: manners, or cleanliness, should be reported to me. Rest assured bad behaviour will be corrected by me."

The fear of God was in Frank now, for he was guilty. He did not have a rosary. He turned in misery to Joe and whispered, "Have *you* got a rosary Joe." His friend nodded blankly that he had, and Frank was not sure if he felt better or worse at this news. Joe had his own worries as he asked Frank a whispered question of his own, "Do *you* ever wet the bed Frank?"

A 'thank you' nod from Father Daniel stopped the nun's instructions and he invited Mrs Hinton to take over. She spoke for the benefit of all, but was looking at the children as she explained, "Not all of the host families are here – but we still have the bus, and a little van – and those children whose foster folk aren't here can have another little ride at the end of the allocation." She tapped her board and turned to look at the villagers, who had grouped to face and more closely inspect the sitting children. "Much of this organisation has been done, and most of you know which child you are here to collect." She pointed, "I will be at the table in that corner. If you can see me – one at a time – we can confirm the allocation. With no fuss at all you can be on your way home with your new guests. It's very simple." Rather as an after-thought she added, "Constable Round or myself will call round, as we have time, within the next day or so. Do you have any questions – any matters of general interest please?"

She answered a flurry of questions, and asked them to encourage the children to write a postcard home saying where they were. She confirmed that although ration books, identity cards and clothing coupons were not immediately to hand, she thought that she would be able to pass these on to them within a matter of a day or so, as soon as they were issued, and certainly before they became necessary. "Can we get on with the allocation we have agreed," she continued, and repeated as she walked over to the table that covered the documentation of this exodus. "It's very simple!"

But it was not at all very simple. The pre-allocation already made by the Reception Officers was mostly ignored. The selection process took its own natural course. Several villagers were embarrassed, and some of the children were humiliated as allocation of children to homes was done in the atmosphere of an auction. Joe, who could swear very impressively, murmured to Frank, "Are they buying us, or what? I feel like a bleeding turkey on Bevan's stall at Aston Cross market."

"I'll take that one!" Mrs Graham called out as she claimed pretty Susan Clements. Susan was the only child standing upright in the gathering of sitting children. She was an intelligent ten year old attracting notice by standing separately to the others. Standing thus drew attention to her prettiness; her smart clothes, and her difference. After apprising the middle-aged, smartly dressed woman who had claimed her, she obediently collected her belongings: a small case, and her gas mask. She went with the authoritative woman to the table in the corner of the Hall where Mrs Hinton objected, "But … Mrs Graham, I have you listed for another young girl." She checked her list before looking up to confirm, "Yes, it's Mary Higgins. I'll soon get her for you, and you can get away." Mrs Graham however was already marching out of the hall – with Susan in her wake almost running to keep up. Mrs Graham had made her selection and she refused to change, or even discuss it. This first selection set the pattern for all of the billeting.

"Mrs Jones will you kindly let go of that boy. I have already spoken with him!" Mrs Jackson consolidated her claim by adding, "His name is Harry, and I was just coming back to confirm that he could come with me." Mrs Jackson was a farmer's wife, and being unable to find any boy looking fitter or stronger than 12 years old Harry, she had returned to take possession of him. Mrs Jones surrendered in bad grace, but moved down the line looking for another bargain of a likely lad.

Shy Betty Frome, almost a teenager, dark haired, slim and lovely, found her arm clutched by the 55 year old Eric Evans. He worked as a mechanic, in the corrugated iron garage workshop behind the village petrol pump. He and his father owned the business. Maintaining his hold on Betty's arm, and saying nothing, he took her to the corner table where, an increasingly gloomy, Mrs Hinton sat. Following the ticking of lists he walked his new property, purposefully and silently, through the village. They walked to the gloomy cottage that Eric shared with his elderly parents.

Joe attached himself to Isabel, a pretty, well rounded young woman in her mid-twenties. She patted a baby across her shoulder, while smiling and chatting easily with all around her. She did not object to Joe's adoption of her, but when he tried to introduce her to Frank, she told him sadly that she just did not have room for another boy.

"Get off your arse and get sorted," Joe hissed at Frank, as he passed with Isabel on their way to the table, and indicating a woman standing quietly alone. "Try that one – she looks alright." Frank however remained sitting on the floor where he had been sited. He watched as children, rooms and villagers were matched. He saw brothers and sisters despairingly parted. He noted Betty's abduction. He was watching as Joe left the hall, but the door closed, and he could not see in which direction his friend went. Without much interest he saw accidents pooling where infants sat. He sat in his lonely bubble, and silently watched as the hall became less and less noisy.

Exercising little influence on events the priest, the nun, the policeman, and the WVS lady, could only watch over the mayhem. They had to accomplish shelter and board in an impossibly short time: it had to be completed before darkness fell. Separately, without discussion, they had compiled lists of urgently needed follow-up visits: calls that had to be made as soon as possible. When they studied their lists, on the day following the allocation, they found that their concerns were remarkably similar. Some of the pairings *had* to be rearranged. They were agreed on this, but it would take time – time they did not immediately have – however they did allow themselves satisfaction in what they *had* achieved.

All of the new arrival had beds for the night. All of the kids were safe in houses, and in beds.

Chapter 7

Complete with his small parcel of clothes, his gas mask, and with the camp bed and bedding supplied by the Council, Frank Bourne was deposited at the garden gate which the Harding family shared with their three immediate neighbours. Mrs Harding was waiting there for them. She was not happy about the new lodger being foisted on her, and did not attempt to hide her lack of enthusiasm. The closest she came to a pleasantry was asking the WVS van driver, with heavy sarcasm "Is this the *best* you've got?"

Mrs Hinton, exhausted after a gruelling day, was aching for a hot bath. Feeling limp, and altogether less important now in her WVS uniform, she was in no mood to exchange sarcastic banter with Edna Harding.

She replied with a prim cynicism, "There *was* a choice at the start – but the *pretty* ones soon got picked out." She smiled down at Frank as though to ease the sting of rejection – which in any case he hadn't noticed. "And you can't tell a book from its cover you know. You've got a good little one here." She patted his head, and thought that, although the lad had not won the raffle with this allocation, there were other billets that she was more concerned about.

She smiled at the two forlorn boys still huddled on the van seat: the final pair to be housed. "Let's go lads. We won't win the war talking about it." She got into the van and she drove off, calling, "'Bye Edna. See you soon. 'Bye Frank. See you soon ... Good luck!"

The woman and the boy watched them go. Then Edna

Harding picked up the bed and bedding bundle, and started to walk with Frank towards the terrace of four cottages.

"Pick it up! For Christ's sake. Pick it up; *carry* the bloody parcel – don't drag it in the dirt," she groaned at him. "I've got more than enough washing to do as it is." She studied him as they walked, watching as he struggled with his parcel and gas mask.

"Now listen … Frank ain't it?" He nodded. "We've been lumbered with you. We didn't want you. We don't want you. It's a bloody nuisance having to put you up. You're the biggest bloody nuisance in our lives. Just you behave; you keep from underfoot – or you'll get the belt. You'll be in the little back room with Brian. He's twelve." Adding with satisfaction, "He's a lot bigger than you … Emily's only ten." She added, "Don't you forget that it's Brian's room," and as an afterthought. "They'll be back from school any minute now."

He spoke for the first time as they arrived at the cottage door. She heard his mumbled first words, and repeated them in a disbelieving bellow, "*You want a number two*! Christ – it's started already. You've been here two minutes and you want a shit. She dropped the camp bed and bedding at the threshold, and snatching the parcel from him she threw that down as well, yelling, "Well don't just stand there shitting yourself!" She grabbed his shoulder and growled, "Come with me … the privy's at the end of the garden."

So Frank's initiation into life within a farm labourer's family was his introduction to the privy. The privy, a cess pit housed in a primitive brick and timbered shed, was one of a pair serving the row of four houses in the terrace. Dimly illuminated, by daylight alone – in the hours when daylight was available – it was an intimidating place. The natural light filtered through cracks in the walls, and via a small lozenge opening cut in the door. It was furnished with a single-hole wooden seat that spanned the full width of the structure. The privy was definitively smelly, and it was curtained with spider webbing.

Mrs Harding removed Frank's trousers, and placing them alongside the hole on the seating, she lifted his stiffened little body into place, sitting him over the terrifyingly large hole above the evil pit. "There's the paper," she said, indicating a wad of eight-inch square pieces of newspaper that were threaded onto a wire hook nailed to the side wall. "Now whenever you come in here you've got to leave it tidy," she ordered adding, "for next door." Then, for the first time sensing his abject terror she continued, "You won't fall in … you silly little bleeder. Nobody falls in!"

She left him alone for a few minutes, to his task. Alone, his fear developed into a terror that swamped even his all-alone misery. Why had his mom done this? Why had she sent him away? Why had she sent him to this big woman … this woman with a belt?

He heard noises, and he imagined noises. He heard huge spiders … lurking, moving and pulsing unseen in the dark corners of the privy.

He gasped with relief when Mrs Harding returned. She appeared not to notice, but ordered briskly, "If you've finished … get off. There are plenty of things to do. Bend over; touch your toes. And wipe your arse for Christ's sake." Impatiently she inspected his bottom cleaning when he had finished, jerked his trousers up and left him to hitch his frayed braces into place.

They walked back to the house. Mrs Harding was a perpetually busy woman with never enough time. She never squandered time. During Frank's first and fearful *number two* meeting with the privy she had watered part of their vegetable garden. With an old bucket, kept there for the purpose, she had used rainwater which had drained from the sloping roof of the shed into a large butt. She had seen his fear, had expected him to blart about it. Good job for him that he hadn't.

Chapter 8

A week after Frank met the Harding family Gladys Bourne received two postcards. She was getting ready for work; thinking as she poured her tea, that one of the first things she would buy with her first pay packet would be a china cup and saucer: she would replace the old jam jar with style. She decided that while she was at it, the other jar would be chucked as well; it would be replaced with a proper tea caddy.

The postman rapped on the door. He visited infrequently; few letters were delivered to houses in this district. Because of this there were no letter boxes in Pretoria Court. Lacking a letter box, and getting no immediate response to his loud knocking, the postman was attempting to push the cards under the door. Gladys having difficulty in tying her turban, grumbled as she moved towards the noise. She was still complaining at the retreating postman when she opened the door and picked up the stained and scruffy mail.

There were two cards and they told her where three of her children were. She read them as she finished her jar of tea. At this hurried time of the day, she promised herself that she would study them properly later on. The place names on the cards were new to her, and with only a vague idea where Staffordshire County was, she was entirely ignorant of the localities, their direction or distance.

The first card she read was from a village called Whycham. It was a blunt notification that Miss Rita Bourne was billeted for the duration of the War at Rose Cottage, Orchard Lane, Whycham. She was under the temporary care and guardianship of Miss Beatrice Bryant.

Gladys wondered what Miss Beatrice Bryant was like: perhaps a bit posh. Then she mused, 'Rose Cottage sounds like in the pictures! It will be really safe for our Rita at Rose Cottage: really nice in the country.'

In similar style the same card informed her that Miss Jean Bourne was billeted with Mr and Mrs Wilfred Statham, The Butchers, Main Street, Whycham.

'How bloody marvellous,' thought Gladys, 'you've fell on your feet there our Jean, a bloody butchers! How good is that?'

She was nervous of the time passing and the time she had to allow to get to work. This was only the first week of her job, she couldn't be late clocking on. However she quickly scanned the second card before leaving the house. She read it properly when she left Pretoria Court and began her walk to work.

The card was written, and signed by Mary Hinton of the WVS:

Dear Mrs Bourne, I am pleased to let you know that your son Frank is staying with Mr and Mrs Edna Harding, and their children Brian and Emily, at their cottage. The address is No 2 Home Farm Terrace, Roslington. I hope that you can drop Frank a line, I know that he would love to hear from you. I saw him yesterday and he is well. Yours truly, Mary Hinton (Mrs)

'Now that's really nice,' thought Gladys as she waited for a fully loaded tram to pass before she crossed the road, 'Our Frank's among a nice family there, and there's this Mary Hinton looking after him as well.'

She wondered again what Beatrice Bryant was like: was she old, young, living on her own perhaps before Rita moved in? She comforted herself with the thought that they were all safely in the country. She stepped up her pace, 'Can't be late on my second day!'

With the postman hammering on the door at that time in the morning her day had started in a panic, but Gladys allowed herself to feel happy now. The cards reconnected her to her kids. She conceded that the postman hadn't really *hammered* at the door: he had knocked, but he had startled her.

Now and then, but often enough to be familiar, letters delivered to the slum neighbourhood came with the legend 'BY HAND' on the envelope. These were delivered *by hand* of a tough looking man, who did hammer rather than rap on doors. She had no reason to expect any such visit, but the innate fear of him was real for her and most of her neighbours.

Her panic reaction to the arrival of the morning post had been instinctive. Now, in the happiness of the morning and the luxury of her innocence, Gladys allowed herself to think about the bailiff: the deliverer of mail that it could have been. Safe and guilt free in her wage earning respectability, she *could* think about the bailiff. He was another symbol of the rough and tough neighbourhood: someone to be scared of, but also one of the colourful experiences of the place. Life here was hard, but you couldn't say that it was uneventful.

Inevitably the bailiff wore a bowler hat. The bowler was a badge of his authority, and it emphasised his law abiding respectability. It did nothing to disguise his determination to get the unpaid account settled, nor did it diminish his physical presence. Usually, it was the landlord who commissioned the bailiff, and the door hammering. Many of those living in Pretoria Court had, at some time been in arrears of rent. They had first-hand knowledge of the fear that was cowering behind the hammered door.

Did it presage a 'moonlight flit' that night? Whose handcart would be borrowed or hired for a few pence? The family, with few possessions to slow them down, could be rattling away in the middle of the night. They would stack everything they owned; it would be piled high on the cart that they pushed and pulled together.

Those who had willing relatives or friends would have farmed out most of the kids ahead of the flit. So it was the husband and the wife alone, who had to make the dramatic escape run. They would curse the metal shod wooden wheels which, with the unfriendly cobbles of the road, noisily announced to all of Birmingham that they were on the Flit.

Often, in the bedding which topped the handcart's load, a baby would be nesting. Clearly it was there for its comfort and safety, and because of the inseparable love and attention it needed, but in a secondary role – and only if they failed to move quickly enough – perhaps the baby might provide a little poignant defence against a bloody nose.

Her third shift at the factory was a gruelling day of concentration and unaccustomed physical exertion. It left Gladys weary, hungry, and very tired. She thought of the limited larder in the dark, cold and empty house that she was walking back to. Thinking about the potato and onion which she could cook, and the bread which was all she had to pad it out with, wasn't an exciting prospect. Gladys easily persuaded herself into a change of plan – two penny worth of chips at Garry Pearce's chip shop in Cheston Road. She laughed at Gary's banter, and dared him to throw in some deep-fried scratchings. The scratchings, bits of batter which had fallen into the fat at an earlier fish frying, were always in demand, because when available they were free. It wasn't a feast but it would occupy her belly for a time at the end of this hard fought day.

She was really looking forward to getting her feet up. She would light the fire; make tea; spread two slices of bread with lard and salt, and with the chips, and the scratchings, make a worthwhile meal.

This modest anticipation was shattered as she turned into Pretoria Court. She was no longer alone.

Chapter 9

Gladys's face dropped when she found that her daughter Ellie was outside the house. She was obviously waiting for her. It could only be with more bad news. With more of an acknowledgement than a greeting she led her daughter into the dark house.

A penny had to be found and put into the meter before she could light the gas mantle in the wall sconce. Other than candles it was the only light in the house. Gladys always tried to manage without lighting the gas. Going to bed when it became dark outside was a great economy. It saved on gas and coal, and by conserving body energy and heat – which otherwise demanded fuelling with food – it saved yet more cash. Tonight the popping, hissing gas light mantle quickly burned white. The peripheral shadows it created made the room dramatic, but less stark.

Ellie had claimed the one upholstered chair, and sat silently picking at a hole in the cloth. She and her brother Dave had salvaged the chair from the Salford dump many months ago. They had roared with laughter all the way home, Dave like a great tortoise with the chair on his back. The chair showed its history with stains and rips, but it was quite comfortable.

Gladys sat at the table on one of the two wooden chairs there. She unfolded the parcel: a newspaper wrapping that had kept her chips warm on her walk home, and picking at the chips she carved two slices from the loaf of bread that she rested on her hip. When the bread slices were spread with lard she built them into a thick chip-filled sandwich. With her mouth full she spoke at last to her daughter.

"Been at work since seven," she explained. "I'm bloody starving." She looked at Ellie who was unusually quiet. Normally by this time into any one of their meetings they would have been arguing, or more than arguing, they would be rowing.

"Have you eaten?" she asked. "What's up Ellie? Has the bastard left you? ... Oh I do hope so!" The bastard could only be Les. Why the hell did she marry the little runt? Gladys looked over at Ellie who remained silent. She couldn't discern any big change in her shape: she was – of course – pregnant. She held her tongue and concentrated on the chip sandwich, but she was no longer enjoying it. Her instinct was to hurl words at her daughter, but she held the words back. She had hurled them before: many times she had told Ellie that she was throwing her life away. That having kids was following the same pattern that she herself had set. And it wasn't worth it!

Not yet twenty one and her first daughter Ellie had been forced to get married. Because that little prick Leslie Pinter had got her into an alley one night. She had devoured every word he murmured, in that grotty entry way. She had believed him: he was deeply in love with her; she was the loveliest thing in his life; he would always protect her, and provide for her. He loved her so much; he couldn't stop kissing her, and feeling her. And ... he could wait no longer to see and feel those tits: the tits which kept him awake each night. Well she had had her fumble in that foul alley way, and now she was pregnant, and not only pregnant, she was married. As expected she had followed the Code, and now she was tied for life to a no-good thug.

Gladys sat in silence: there was no 'told you so' satisfaction in her thoughts. The mother despaired, but instead of starting a row she asked again, "Have you eaten? Do you want some of this? I'll get the fire going in a minute and we can have some tea." With a shake of her head her daughter declined the offers of food, but she accepted her mother's conciliatory attitude when she once more gently asked, "What's up Ellie?"

Then Ellie allowed her tears to come, and Gladys sitting across from her, silently encouraged her daughter to cry. Quietly she wrapped up the debris of her unsatisfactory meal and used the greasy parcel of waste to start a fire in the small black leaded range that the room boasted. With the blackened kettle placed onto the struggling smoky fire she returned to her seat at the table, took a packet of ten Park Drive cigarettes and a box of matches from the pocket of her wrap-round apron, and lit one with a deeply inhaled satisfaction.

Ellie rose to her offer, "You want one?" Her tears had stopped; she walked to where her mother sat and took a cigarette from the opened packet on the table. In silence she lit this, using the glowing end of her mother's cigarette and then returned to the armchair. As Ellie's unhappy tale unfolded over the next hours, they smoked all of the cigarettes. They would have smoked more, if more had been available.

Les *had* left her – but not by choice. He had been taken to Steelhouse Lane police station. He had been drinking at his local, The Grapes in Vine Street. Always noisy, full of smoke, spit and sawdust: it was his favourite pub. With the help of several pints of mild and bitter beer, and goaded on by his drinking mates, he had become involved in an almost predictable brawl with some Irish workmen. When he staggered home, to the room they had in his mom's house in Lynton Road, he was in a mess. His face was covered in blood and bruises; his nose looked to have been broken; he was nursing an arm that he groaned had also been broken – and the pain was increasingly hitting in – as the anaesthetic of the alcohol he had drunk wore off.

The Police had arrived shortly afterwards. Tracking him down had called for little detection work on their part. Leslie Pinter was well known to them; well known to the men in the public bar of the Grapes, and well known to the onlookers outside the pub. Starting as a one-on-one altercation between Les and an Irish labourer, the jostling rapidly involved others wanting a fight. There were no neutrals there.

The landlord and his cronies, using thumps, threats and violent language, wrestled the incipient fight towards the door and ejected the main players, before standing back to protect the property, as spectators. A crowd quickly gathered to watch the entertainment as the brawl erupted out of the pub and spilled into the street. More and more men joined the audience. This grew rapidly, quickly losing the defining edge separating it from the melee, and promising to become a full scale riot.

Several of the men from the growing crowd becoming involved, as they recognised friends and factions, 'needing help' in the fight. It was an 'all in' nationalist war fought viciously with weapons of fists, boots, bottles and glasses. It was great entertainment for the people of Aston: it brought some colourful variety, into jobless grey lives.

Police soon arrived in numbers, and they rapidly blanketed the mob conflagration. The leading, and most vicious rioter was identified. He was no longer on the scene, but everybody in the locality knew the wiry, arrogant, rowdy, drinking man called Les. He was not a popular figure. Enough of them knew exactly where he lived in Lynton Road and they were happy to pass on the information. The Police however needed no directions after his name had been revealed: they had called at that Lynton Road address before.

When they had him cornered within the house, and with the experience gained on previous painful visits, the police wasted no time, and gave no sympathy to the sullen afflicted villain. After a perfunctory, ritual knock – with a truncheon on the front door – it was smashed open and three brawny policemen piled into the small front room.

It was no contest. The cursing, screaming man was forced face down, in agony, onto the floor boards. With cold ruthless efficiency, he was swiftly handcuffed. The sweating policeman ignored his profane promises of revenge as they manhandled him. Les's curses and threats changed to howls of pain, as inevitably his broken arm got in the way of the police efforts: they made no allowance for the obvious agony he was in.

As they dragged him out, and into the waiting police car, they brushed aside the feeble tearful protests of his wife. The distraught Ellie was told that he was being taken to Steelhouse Lane, the main police station in the city. She was also told that it had been much more than a regular drunken 'bundle' at the Grapes. Some of the rioters were already in custody at Steelhouse Lane. A greater number of them were in the adjacent Steelhouse Lane General hospital.

"You've got a Bad Un there Missus," an unsympathetic policeman told her. "He was in the thick of it … and he was the start of it … this could end up in a murder charge!"

When Ellie went to the station the next day she was told that, 'so far' no one had died. Her husband had just been taken under escort to the General, to have his arm 'seen to'.

"He does cry a lot when *he's* in pain don't he?" the Desk Sergeant volunteered in pseudo sympathy, "Nobody in cells could get a wink last night." Quizzed by Ellie he agreed that Les's arm *was* broken, cynically pondering, "I wonder how *that* happened."
She was allowed to wait in the busy reception area.

Waiting for Les to be returned to the station, she sat on a rigidly slatted wooden bench for more than three hours. She was able to laugh with her mom when she told her about this. She described the bench and the long wait with the additional comment, "I reckon my arse looks like the tram terminus now!"

The Desk Sergeant, having watched her through those hours, felt sorry enough to allow her five minutes with Les when he was back at the station. Ellie said the pain of that long night showed in his eyes, but she had to agree with her mother that he would not have learned any lesson from it. Leslie Pinter was, is, and always would be Les. He was waiting now to appear before the Magistrates.

Mother and daughter skated on thin ice during a long, much repeated discussion of Ellie's situation. Gladys was emphatically of the opinion that she should have an abortion: now – before it was too late, and too dangerous. She knew how she could get this organised. There was enough experience in Pretoria court alone, to ensure that it was a reputable woman who could be called in: somebody safe; with a perfect safety record. But it had to be organised quickly. These things can't wait.

Ellie was totally against such an expedient indignantly telling her mother, "Well *you* didn't! And you had enough chances with all of the kids *you've* had!"

She then reacted to the grimly contorting face of her mother, imploring, "You DIDN'T … *Did you Mom?*"

The direction of their conversation altered without further mention of abortion. It was not an option that Ellie could contemplate. Instead Gladys told her that the Catholic Church could help. They never wanted to take in *older* kids, but they would take her to a place, 'somewhere' to have her baby.

She thought – No she knew – it was so! There was a Catholic Home somewhere in Wales, for women and girls in trouble, like her: where she would be well looked after, and the baby would be well looked after. And then – the baby would be brought up – without her. She would not even have to see it!

Ellie would not contemplate this shocking solution either. "We're having our baby," she shouted at Gladys. "You've had yours; Les and me will have ours. I know what you're saying, but it will not be like that with us … WE don't *have* to keep having kids: neither of us is Catholic," she ended weakly. "You *can prevent* kids from happening. And you can still be in love. I will *not* sell my baby to the Catholics. And I won't kill him either! I want this baby!"

Gladys was crying now, softly and from the bottom of her being. God she wanted a fag! Ellie hadn't said it but she knew that only Frank, Rita and Jean were christened Catholics. Gladys in the desperation of absolute poverty had pleaded for help, at the church of England church, the Catholic church, and even the workhouse. In return for help, and meagre help it turned out to be, she thought ruefully, she had converted to the Roman Catholic faith.

In order to seal the bargain she had taken Jean, Rita, and Frank, the three youngest of her children, into the catholic school and into the church with her. They had been instructed, and christened, and would be confirmed as Catholics. Additionally she had agreed, as part of the deal that any other children she might have would be brought up in the catholic religion also. With the solemnity demanded she had vowed to this effect. Standing at the altar rail, leaning against it for support and close to collapse, she had vowed this – knowing that there *would not* be any more children; *could not be* any more children.

'Yes Ellie,' she thought, 'I've let it slip, and you know now. I *did* call in *that* Mrs Smith. I did lie on this very table and I did see the knitting needle and I did let this enormous animal of a woman do what *had* to be done … what *had* to be done to my body. You were all at your gran's. She knew of course! It was your gran who got it arranged … and she had to know. And Bill knew: your dad knew. He was dead against us going catholic. He talked it out with Dave, Charlie and Joan – and you Ellie – and he persuaded you all not to! We could have had a bit more help from them if *all* of us had converted. Your dad – your precious dad – couldn't feed and clothe us properly. All he *could* provide us with was his bloody principles.'

She realised that Ellie was quiet now. She thought again of her husband, and of that dreadful time, 'But he *did* get the two pounds for Mrs Smith. I couldn't have another kid – Frank had to be the last!' Aloud, seeming to address the table she spoke with gentleness, "I listened to *my* mother, and she was right. Ellie … You ought to listen to me!"

All crying had stopped. The fire was still burning: she would keep it in now ready for the morning, which she could see from the cheap alarm clock was not far away. "I've got to get to work in the morning Ellie. We'll have another cup of tea and then I've got to get some sleep. It aint easy at Albrights, I must get some rest. I'm not going to bugger up this job! You'd better sleep here tonight: there's plenty of room now the kids have gone."

Both of them were exhausted.

Ellie became suddenly aware that there *was* plenty of room in the house. "Have you heard from them yet?" she asked. "Have they told you where they are? How is little Frank?"

Her mother felt in her apron pocket and passed the two cards to her. Having read them Ellie asked her, "Can I borrow these; I'll copy the addresses and let you have them back tomorrow." She put them into her pocket. Somehow she never managed to give them back.

"At least that's one big worry gone," said Gladys. She livened up the old tea leaves with a few more fresh ones, and made the promised tea. "The kids are alright: they're in good hands. They're being properly looked after. They're *happy*, and they're safe."

They exchanged "Good Nights," with Gladys commenting, "It is so good to know that the kids are OK – they're safe – in the country!"

Chapter 10

Frank grew up very quickly in that first year that he spent with the Harding's. He learned the value of anonymity. He always 'did as he was told' – and he found that he was frequently able to avoid being in situations and places where he *could* be told. He devised a technique that allowed him to cope with the fearsome privy.

His set procedure included leaving number twos to the last minute, and never visiting the place at dusk or in the dark. When he *had* to go; when he had to sit over that dreadful hole in the planking, he concentrated his vision on the friendly day-lit lozenge in the door. He kept his eyes closed as much as possible. He never looked for spiders, mice, rats, or the source of creaks and scrabbling – and he always piddled *behind* the privy.

He quickly learned that Mrs Harding had 'moods'. It was best to see these coming, and then, like everybody else, including Mr Harding, keep out of her way. He learned how *not* to cry: how to be desperately unhappy without crying, how not to think of mom. Most importantly, for longer and longer periods of time, he learned how to avoid Mrs Harding, *and* Brian: how not to be a victim. Frank developed gumption, and a major part of this developing initiative was the cunning to keep his gumption hidden and unadvertised: to exist without being noticed.

Bill Harding was a farm labourer, and the cottage that he and his family called home was tied to his job. It was the only job he knew and an inevitable occupation for him when he left the local school after unremarkable years there. Being capable, strong and willing made him good at his trade. He was well regarded and respected at the farm and in the village, although the family was at the rough end of the village social scale.

Bill's job made him automatically exempt from call-up into the armed forces. Secretly and guiltily he regretted this exemption. He wanted to fight: more exactly he wanted to get away for a while. He wanted to escape the dull routine and hard labour of the old-fashioned farm to which he was bound, the job that exempted him from conscription. But he wouldn't be called up to fight in the war. He could not get away from the farm: the farm with its day-on, week-on, year-on, grind-down sameness of muscle straining labour. Monotonous chores in all weathers, to win a sad pay packet come Saturday.

He had a recurring and guilty dream of escape: of exchanging a thirteen-year-old marriage – and an abrasive angular woman of thirty-two – for a rifle, comrades and adventure. In truth he was fond of his wife and kids, but they had bricked him into a corner of inescapable monotonous hard labour.

Sunday was the only colour in Bill's week, the day when one routine was replaced by another. The Sunday routine with the kids quiet – under threat of the belt – and the luxury of a lie-in. To follow a tasty, unhurried and mainly fried breakfast. Some forenoon work on his own account, perhaps some easy paced gardening; repairing a bike puncture or fixing his *own* gate hinges. Then at about noon time he would wash in the kitchen sink, change into Sunday trousers and shirt and saunter to the Cherry Tree. In the bar there he would have two, perhaps three, rarely four, pints of mild. Swapping and matching jokes and boasts with the limited friends, in his limited life. He would recall the banter during his walk home, enjoying the glow in his head and belly. The beer inspired extroversion giving him freedom to greet and exchange chat with any passing barge on the Trent and Mersey canal.

Home and Bill, glowing with his earlier beer, was ringleader at the week's Sunday dinner event. Plenty of vegetables; Yorkshire pudding and, as it was plated up, he would orchestrate a chorused demand for "TBG!" Thick Brown Gravy to supplement the roast meat. There was usually a duff to round the feast off. The pudding inevitably, and happily complete with Lumpy Yellow Custard – brought to the table to shouted salutes of "LYC!"

It was the best day of the week – a happier place for the children – with a different mood set by the usually introverted father on his precious day off. Frank sat back in his 'listen-only' anonymity and relaxed as Edna relinquished her unhappy authority to the benign head of the house. Then, with the dishes washed, come rain or sunshine, the kids were banished. Brian and Emily despatched to Sunday school; Catholic Frank to heaven knows where, but out; away from the house. And Bill's Sunday afternoon lost in bed with Edna.

Plans of working a farm of own had drifted into mere daydreams a long time ago: the dreams becoming less focussed as they became less and less attainable with the passing of years and the birth of the children.

This evacuee was yet another intrusion into the space that he yearned for, but … he did feel a bit sorry for the sad little sod. He looked so unhappy – *all* of the time. He didn't say much, but Bill hadn't heard him crying or moaning. Brian was thirteen now and he still moaned and cried a lot. Emily had her moments too, but the new urchin was quiet. And he kept himself small – although Edna caught hold of him now and again.

Bill remembered when Frank *had* cried: the one time. Bill had had to strap him, so crying then didn't count against him. Any boy – or man – would cry, if only from humiliation, when his pants were downed and the leather razor strop – the Belt – was applied. Bill hadn't laid it on very hard. In truth he was more amused than angry, but Frank had been rumbled and he had to be strapped.

It was a good yarn for his mates at the Sunday pint. Frank had been sent to the shop one evening. He had been given a silver sixpence to pay for ten Woodbines and a box of matches. There should have been two pence change, but the boy squandered a penny of the change on a poke of mixed nuts and raisins. They had somehow escaped the rationing, and had sat on the shop's counter in a tray of similar, irresistible triangular packets. When challenged about the penny short change the little bugger had said that matches had *gone up a penny*!

One stripe was given for stealing; one for lying so badly and stupidly, and one extra for taking a long time on the guilty walk home eating the booty. Without amusement Bill recalled Brian's mocking hilarity at the strapping. With the belting done he had himself pulled Frank's shorts up – to block Brian's view of the sadly reddened bottom.

Frank kept quietly out of each day's traffic as much as he could, but he couldn't keep out of the way all of the time. It was then – when in the spotlight – that he suffered the most. Humiliation, often casual and unthinking, was sparked mainly by him just being there. His crime, with the rest of the uninvited incomers, was being there in their village. He was an evacuee, an easy miserable target. He was an unattractive townie urchin who wasn't wanted in Roslington. The village of miners and farmers was a close bordered society: a hardworking, manly place of the colour grey. The village and Mrs Harding in particular, could do without evacuees.

One dark evening shortly after his arrival, Frank was to endure an early humiliation that was to haunt him. He was alone with Mrs Harding. Brian, Emily and their dad had left to visit gran in her house at the other end of the village. Not being family, Frank had been left with Mrs Harding.

When the others had left the house she told him to take his clothes off. "All of them!" She then positioned him in front of the coal fire. She told him on which precise spot he was to stand. She herself sat on the wooden chair placed at the side of the fireplace. She started to silently darn socks and soon appeared to be entirely unaware of his pathetic presence.

She had bullied the scared boy into position. "Stand there! Just you stand there!" Then threateningly she added, "*They've* gone out. *I* can't go out. I get no time to myself; I can't even go to see my own mother."

She continued loudly, shouting, "Because we can't leave you here on your own." She continued ranting at the wide-eyed boy, "You're a bleeding nuisance … always around, always underfoot, *and always so bleeding miserable.* Just you stand still … and stand *very* still!" He *had* stood still – very still, and very silent, and unhappy – for a long time.

Mainly by bartering with working miners in this mining village, the Hardings enjoyed cheap and plentiful coal. The fire was well stacked, and it had burned brightly. The right side of his body: his leg, thigh and arm, reddened very quickly. He had wanted to whimper and cry, but he was not able to, the powerful presence of the woman had stifled the whimper. He was in purgatory.

In his increasing pain Frank concentrated his attention on a small colourful ornament. It stood on the mantle shelf of the range, and he had bought it with the sixpence given to him by his mother. She had given him that tanner when he had last seen her; when they were last together.

After their arrival at Burton, while waiting for buses for their further travel, it had been suggested to the evacuees, that buying a little gift would be a nice surprise for their new 'mom'. At the suggestion those with money immediately milled about a small stall at the station. Never having had money before, Frank had never before bought anything. The concept of buying and giving presents was new to him. But eventually he had picked out, and paid his sixpence for, the three inch, brightly painted plaster figure. It was a pretty girl with yellow hair, ever so red lips, and a short flounced out dress over little plump legs.

He hated that little girl now. He so regretted buying her. She was laughing at him. The present he had given to Mrs Harding gaily preened. Without a care, with no concern, she was laughing even now, a happy witness of his humiliation and pain.

Eventually he was compelled to sway away, very slightly easing his buttocks from the intense heat of the fire. Mrs Harding had looked up instantly, accusingly scanning his pathetic, paining body. Some few minutes later he had been released. He was sent to bed: to the grey blanket on the camp bed in Brian's room. There to moan softly in discomfort and self-pity. Not loudly enough that she could hear, but a gentle croon that did, at last, help him to find some relief in a fitful sleep.

Later in the night – with Brian soundly asleep in his bed on the other side of the room – Frank painfully eased himself out of the bed. He stood by the window and lowered his forehead onto the glass. It was cold; it felt good. He pulled himself on to the window cill and earned some relief. Firstly his thigh, and then his arm, and his bottom, he pressed them, in turn, against the cold, cold, friendly window glass.

Chapter 11

Today was a spring day. Frank was standing almost naked in front of the unlit range. Bare-footed on the cold brown linoleum floor and wearing a shirt only, nothing else. He was not cold. He did not feel the cold: he felt nothing but sullen humiliation. Unbidden and unhappily his mind wandered once more. He had been here before in this exact same spot. A long time ago, not long after he came to this place, before he was seven even. Then the fire *had* been burning. Then his only friend had been a cold window.

The rear room of the cottage was small and sparsely equipped. He looked with dumb unhappiness at the whitewashed walls. He saw the three unmatched wooden chairs at the scrubbed deal table, the small rag-rug, and the shiny proud cooking range.

He had black leaded this to its present shine just yesterday: at the time he had felt pride in a job well done. He regretted its fine appearance now. A net curtain covered the bottom half of the room's only window. Through the window, hanging on the wall outside, he could see the long zinc bath.

He focussed his attention on the single adornment in the room, a framed copy of the etching, *The Martyrs Farewell*. The anguished martyr was beautiful; she was gazing with wide tear-filled eyes at an infant child. They were separated by the bars of her cell window; she held her baby's tiny hand through the bars. Frank knew the scene well. He had studied it during his months in this house. It was satisfyingly sad. He tried to stay there – in the cell, with the martyr and her baby – but he slipped back into reality. His eyes were drawn back to the window, and they focussed on that looming, zinc, bungalow bath hanging outside.

Every few weeks or so Bath Day would be announced. Bath day was always on a Saturday afternoon. The bath would be taken down from its nail. The hearth rug would be moved away, and the long steel bath placed in front of the kitchen range. There, in all seasons a well stoked coal fire burned on bath days.

Fired up earlier in the day, the boiler in the yard's wash-house provided buckets of hot water. These were carried into the house, emptied into the bath, and finally tuned with cold water from the kitchen sink tap. When Mrs Harding was satisfied that the temperature was just as she wanted it, the kids were evicted, the curtain was drawn, the door bolted, and she would take her own bath. It wasn't a luxury, but quickly dispensed with. The last buckets of the wash house hot water would then be brought indoors to replenish the long tin bath and restore its temperature for her husband's soak.

He was exactly on time. He was never late leaving the farm on appointed bath nights, and the bath would be ready for him when he arrived home. The second, rather more leisurely bath was his.

Emily would take her bath next. When she had finished, and was getting dressed in her bedroom, Brian and Frank would be called in from the yard for *their* ritual ablutions. Brian would be first – Mrs Harding kneeling by the bath in the best position to very thoroughly scrub his head and body. Brian always complained noisily throughout his time in the bath: protesting about the rough treatment, and always about soap in his eyes. His complaints fell on deaf ears. His mother ignored him at bath time.

With her son discharged to dry, and dress, and finish his moaning upstairs, it was Frank's turn to step into the rapidly cooling and by now very grey water. He sat down in almost cold water.

'JESUS ...Holy Mary ... God ...' the first bath time, suddenly

and without warning, his head had been pushed down between his legs – and it had been held there … and held there … held in a vice like grip that ridiculed his struggles to get free. He thrashed at the water with body, arms and legs trying desperately to pull him up – all the time panicking to hold his breath – but choking.

At last he was released … spluttering and gasping … and had had his bottom, his face and his arm slapped hard by the indignant woman. "You little sod! … You ungrateful bugger … look at all this mess … none of the others make this fuss … emptying the bath everywhere. Get the mop and get it cleaned up … and you can empty the bath … and without making more mess than you have already. There's the bucket. Empty the bath with the bucket first – you daft prat – *then* mop the floor! Now get on with it!"

He heard her grumbling as she went upstairs. There to put on a dry wrap-round apron, and complain to Bill that he had to get rid of that bleeding monster. "You should see the mess he's made in the kitchen … Bloody obvious he's never had a bath before … filthy little bugger!"

The same torture was applied on every bath day thereafter. The first time it had happened it was terrifying. It became very much more frightening, because now he knew, and anticipated, and waited for it to happen again. His experience made the waiting time unbearable! Each bath torment was prolonged while his rigid body was flannelled, roughened and reddened by the grunting, angry woman – his arms, legs, chest, back then – "Stand up!" That was for the intimate body scrub. "Sit down!" – And the bar of hard yellow soap was pummelled through his hair. And then the drowning! *'Oh my God!'* – Sometimes he would be ducked and drowned for a second time.

Emptying the bath was his job. With the torment over it was almost a relief – not quite a survival celebration – to take the bucket, scoop the bath water into it, and slowly and carefully empty the bath, going out to the yard drain to discharge each bucket.

It was at this point, after Frank's first experience of bath day, that Mr Harding, his after bath rest destroyed by his wife's noisy complaints, had been attracted to the bedroom window. Looking out he saw the naked boy shuffling with the bucket, emptying it in the drain gully. Immediately he shouted to him, but not unkindly, "Get dry and get your clothes on before you do that you daft bugger!"

His wife commented in her victimised tone of voice, "He *knows* bloody well that the bloody neighbours can see him!" She was incensed by her husband's rough caring humanity. He didn't know just how much she hated the boy. And her hatred for the boy grew with Bill's ignorance of her hatred. He should be on her side!

But now after the baths Frank was at least dressed. He was dressed for the neighbours perhaps, but he was warmer, and almost dry, while completing the final chore of bath night. Humiliated and scared, suppressing the fear within him, keeping any sign of unhappiness for his grey blanket, on the camp-bed, in Brian's room.

Today the sun was shining; it reflected off that bath hanging on the outside wall. Frank looked away from the window; he did not glance at the sad martyr holding her baby's hand; he didn't see the uncaring plaster figurine with the yellow hair. He looked down. He looked down at nothing. He was once again in the shameful spot that had witnessed: first his roasting, then his drowning, and now this, his latest tribulation. It was the same fearsome spot – in front of that fire. Mrs Harding sat in the same chair.

Today her sister's eldest daughter Mary was sitting with her. They were talking seemingly without pause while the older woman stitch-repaired a rent in Frank's trousers.

"Stop fidgeting!" Edna Harding made time to grumble at him, "And there's no need for you to clutch your bits like that. Stand up straight – you're too young and stupid to be shy." Then more sharply she ordered, "Drop your hands down you young stupid sod! And stop playing the hard-done-by. Stop playing with yourself! You've not got anything to frighten us here. *You* tore the bloody trousers, you tyke, so stand still there while I put them right." Frank slowly lowered his cupped hands. With increasing shame he knew that the teenage Mary was looking at him – and she was looking at it.

Normally growing-up is a seamless, steady and slow process, whereby the body and the mind together absorb knowledge and experience. They strengthen, develop, and mature together. But this catalytic moment was a jolt to his being that changed Frank's life in a moment. Misery became anger: he grew up a lot in that moment.

With resolve, and a determination not previously experienced, he slowly raised his head. He challenged the girl with an intense, unblinking stare. Mary averted her gaze; Frank gently replaced his cupped hands.

Edna Harding was preoccupied and unaware of this happening. She looked to pile further humiliation on this bloody, sullen, shit nuisance that she hated. "Say ELECTRICITY Frank!" she ordered, "Listen to this Mary. Don't it beat the lot?" and she repeated sharply, "say ELECTRICITY!" Frank could not say electricity. Although he secretly practised he just could not pronounce the word correctly. He looked at the small fuse-box fitted over the front door. This was where his torment had started. In an unguarded moment he had answered Emily Harding's question about the box, telling her it was the place where *electrickity* entered the house.

Emily's Mom had heard him, and his mispronunciation made her howl with laughter, it was a rare treat for her. Now she often wheeled out the incident attempting to amuse the family, or prompt any visitor to laugh.

Frank mumbled it now for Mary, "Electrickity," he said, and immediately lost his recently won strength, and superiority over her. "Again," said Edna. He could only repeat the mind blocked pronunciation, "Electrickity." "Have another go!" she cried, "Say it again!"

"Elec ...TRICKITY," he shouted.

It was loud, defiant, and glorious. Unrepentant he once more moved his head to challenge Mary with his fierce eyes. He saw that Mary wasn't laughing. It was not funny. Her body language showed that she had not found it at all funny.

With this disappointing lack of support from her niece Mrs Harding didn't laugh either. She completed the repair, bit off the cotton and threw the short trousers back to Frank.

"There's a pile of newspapers under the sink," she grumbled, "go and cut them up for the privy."

Chapter 12

With the arrival of the evacuees Roslington Village Hall became All Saints Roman Catholic School, and it was overcrowded from the start. Having attracted evacuee Catholic children from several miles around the village more than a hundred children attended the school. .

Father Daniel nominally had two teachers: Sister Alice and another nun, but the children hardly got to know the second nun, because invariably and very soon after her arrival, she would be replaced by yet another wide eyed Initiate Nun sent from the shoulder- shrugging religious order in Birmingham. At Head Office, the Birmingham Convent, they knew Sister Alice well, and knew the intolerant standards imposed by her. So as one nun was despatched to replace the latest incompatible failure, yet another unfortunate was groomed to replace *her*.

This routine was an approved and tolerable way to avoid the good Sister's resignation – and obviate her return to them and the Convent. In wartime spirit the Convent staff used the acronym SAFE: Save Alice For Evacuees, or more cruelly: Sister Alice Fodder Exchange.

So in the main it fell to Father Daniel to supervise, teach and manage the school. He had the untrained assistance of two teenage girls, and the grudging support of Sister Alice, whose dogmatic teaching methods created much friction between them. She saw that her main role in the school was to provide spiritual instruction, guidance, and discipline. Father Daniel annoyed her constantly. He suggested that her use of indoctrination and correction were less effective than instruction and persuasion. She did not change. She continued to boss the occasional, temporary young nun and she maintained law and order in her own way.

The school comprised three classes that were defined more by a child's age rather than ability; however Frank rapidly progressed out of the youngest group because, amazingly quickly, he learned to read, and by rote he was able to cope with arithmetic. Comprehension came to him rather more slowly, but with his exceptional promotion he was able to sit next to Joe – Sister Alice permitting. He resignedly paid the fee for sharing this particular desk, by taking the slaps and pinches that came with the seat, and which were always in striking range of wherever Joe was.

Catechism class was the fearful, awful start to every school morning. Sister Alice hammered the creed of the Catholic Church into the children, testing them daily on inflexible beliefs that most of them could not comprehend. She filled their minds with Purgatory and Hell. Flames – burning flesh that never burned away – endless writhing and screaming. She painted pictures of their own progression towards this damnation. Inevitably they were going to burn for their sins.

There *was* hope for *some* of them. Some, just a few of the *less* sinful, would have to burn for a shorter time in Purgatory, a time proportionate to the sins they committed on Earth. Others, *and she could name them*, would be in Hell, to burn forever. There was no escape! The omniscience of God was total. He saw everything, and He knew everything.

One day Joe earned a nasty slapping and pinching. He had asked, innocently, if God's presence everywhere was the same ability that Sister Alice had. She knew everything about everything, and everybody. She had the same God's knowledge of *everything* that was going on.

The Catholic Faith demanded total belief without question. The Sister could not see any purpose for life, other than as a rocky path to heaven. The rockier the path was through life the better chance you had of salvation. It was very clear to her that young minds were cess pits. Formed by the Original Sin at birth, and then rapidly compacted by the sludge from sinful parents, and compounded by the filthy way that they lived, in their filthy slums. The young minds had first to be emptied, and then carbolically scoured, before they could be filled with The Truth. The Truth had to be understood, before it could be learned and become part of their being.

Many young minds in her care could not comprehend and, in the entire lives, would never comfortably understand the concept of the Almighty Holy Trinity: a Father, and a Son, AND a Ghost as well! Catechism words and phrases allowed them to pretend otherwise in the presence of the Nun. Fortunately Sister Alice believed enough for all of them. All *they* had to do was be word perfect when she questioned them on their beliefs.

Logically the children named this first hour of every school day – PURGATORY. After registration every child, without exception, was given instruction and tested on the Catechism. There was no escape from the Church handbook. The youngest, and some of the more slowly minded of the children, did not appreciate the sophisticated humour in that purgatory title. They really did think that the dreaded hour was literally *the Purgatory*.

Sadly the aphorism was naively betrayed by a young innocent: a five years old girl. When she heard the Catechism class renamed as Purgatory, she thought that at last she *could* understand! She no longer had to be terrified by the vivid pictures of the flames of Purgatory and Hell painted by Sister in the first hour of each day. She resolved to listen hard every day, so that she could learn and perhaps further understand the fearful dogma that Sister hammered into them. This early lesson in every school day was not pleasant for her, but it was much better than being set fire to!

At the first opportunity she proudly displayed her newly acquired understanding. Sister Alice heard the infant girl declaring,

"Purgatory isn't *too* bad: I don't like Catechism class Purgatory, but it isn't as bad as burning! If I *had* to I could stay in Purgatory for a bit longer – like just enough to get rid of my sins – so I could go straight to heaven." Sister Alice was not amused, and they all suffered.

The Nun suffered too though, for she glimpsed that she was wasting her time on these unworthy little beasts. The big fearsome nun was not aware that a separate catechism was being formulated by some of the grubby animals under her tutelage.

Frank was not sure about sinning. Although he vowed, in regular Acts of Contrition, 'Never to sin again,' he could not avoid sins: they just happened. He edited his breathless Contrition in order to make it real and possible: *O my God because thou art so good I am so sorry that I have sinned against you and I will* **really try** *never to sin again!*

Often he didn't know that he *had* sinned, remaining ignorant of the dreadful danger that he was in, until Sister Alice once again would remind him of his wickedness and, with a slap, pinch of his arm or leg, present him with yet more Rosary penance. She told him that *all* of his sins would be made known to him as he burned in the everlasting flames: ignorance was not an excuse. The only hope was in hours of Rosary prayers, and for the good of his soul Sister Agnes prescribed endless Hail Marys and Lord's Prayers.

Frank gabbled the first part of the prayer: *Hail Mary full of grace the Lord is with thee blessed art thou amongst women and blessed is the fruit of thy womb JESUS* – here pausing and giving a respectful bow at mention of Jesus – before completing the second part of the prayer. This part he understood and he would more slowly recite and sincerely implore: *Holy Mary mother of God Pray for us sinners NOW and at the hour of our death – AMEN.* Frank was not alone: he was not the only miserable, confused, doomed and terrified child. They all were – except Joe.

Joe was an atheist, a philosopher, a great comfort and teacher to his small chum Frank. "Fuck it," he said, startling his young friend with another awesome word that demonstrated his worldliness and wisdom, "You can't win Mate. You're going to have to sin whether you like it or not. You can't help it. If you live and breathe you're going to sin. Any case – you have the Big Sin for ever – Black Cow's Original Sin."

He saw that Frank was puzzled and explained further, "Which is what you get when your Mom and your Dad enjoy making you in the first place! We have all got that one, without even trying! Original Bloody Sin! Whatever! Whatever it is – you have got it. So what chance is there for stupid buggers like us? Forget it – you're going to go there anyway – so enjoy the trip while you're going." He was still bemused but Frank did not seek further enlightenment of the original sin he was carrying. He knew that Joe would explain it all eventually.

Joe then explained his philosophy in some detail to a very impressed Mate. "Do what I've done; I have done it already – I have told HIM I'm not going to join – I don't *want* an immortal soul – *I don't want to live forever.* I want to live and die like the animals do: I want to Live, and then I want to Die ...in that order. Fuck it!" He elaborated, "Sometimes living ain't that good anyway; dying may not be that bad."

The pair had been lying in a corner of the Rec – the recreation ground – when Frank was introduced to this different creed. They had been chewing on hawthorn leaves. They were hungrily convinced that these leaves *could* taste *just a bit* like bread and cheese. Frank soaked up Joe's catechism. It was reasoned; understandable; reassuring and good. It was not only about inescapable sins, and inescapable punishment, and it became more and more clear and attractive the more often they discussed it. At one of their discussions he committed himself.

His decision was taken and he bravely declared this to his mate, "I want to *just die as well Joe* – like the animals – like a *bird* Joe. I wish I could fly – and then just die – just as birds do." Joe considered the statement seriously. He thought this was sound, but then he brought his friend back to earth. "You know, you can't *tell* anybody about this. You will still have to do the catechism and things – you must keep the ugly Black Cow off your back – or you will be burning in hell," and he added, "And that's *before* you die!"

Catechism class was conducted in one of the three rooms occupied by the new school. It was a large bright room with a sign on the door that caused it to remain known as the Colliery Band room. The Band was angry to lose this and one day they arrived at the school in force. They came to remind everyone that the Hall was only temporarily on loan to the Catholics. The building belonged to them as villagers, and the Band room specifically belonged to the Band. To reinforce the point they truculently demanded use of the room for an afternoon of practice. Sister Agnes fumed and spat at Father Daniel, "Can't you *do* something about it?" The Priest however delighted in the excitement that arrived with the part-time musicians. He welcomed the band, and conspired with the bandleader, before announcing an end to classes for the day – "Everything away. Let us make way for music!"

The main hall was again the Band room. Desks and chairs were cleared to the sides of the room, the children sat on the floor, the band noisily set up, and then their practice began. The 'excused-classes' children were attentively quiet as the repertoire unfolded, and after a self-conscious, hesitant start, the rehearsal very quickly became a concert. The band played before their most appreciative audience ever. They warmed and responded to the wide eyed attention and enthusiasm of these young initiates to music, whose very bodies vibrated with the deeply rich and magical sounds. Enveloped in emotive, glorious brass-band noise, the children clapped and cheered every piece played, provoking yet more enthusiastic effort from the musicians.

"Joe …," whispered Frank in a quieter moment between pieces, "Joe … I could cry. Not *sad* cry but I feel funny! Like a happy cry!" There was no way that Joe could admit to a need to cry, but he knew exactly what his mate meant, and he expressed the exhilaration that he too was feeling, "Great ain't it. It's bloody great!" He went on to graphically confide, "It makes me Willy feel funny!"

The Band later declared it was their best ever performance. Their music lingered as salve, in minds painfully grappling with the next morning's dogma class in the same room. A room – that was now just a little different.

The Reverend Humphries called at the school during the show, expecting to witness a showdown between village men and townie Catholics, but the expected confrontation didn't happen, and the Vicar didn't stay long. Sister Alice walked from the band room with him: they made a sad pair: dejected for different reasons. Archie King, the band leader, looking over his animated baton, exchanged broad winks with Father Daniel before another encore was entered into, and the date for the next concert was agreed on.

Later that night Frank prayed to Mary and Jesus. Lying stiff and silent on the truckle camp bed, in the pitch blackness of the small room that he shared with Brian, he cleared his backlog of penances – all awarded by 'the ugly black nun.' Twenty Hail Marys and four Our Fathers, he tried to remember what they were for, but he couldn't. He prayed to Mary first by conscientiously working through his twenty Hail Marys. He apologised for not knowing exactly what his sins had been, and promised sincerely to be better. Then he explained to Mary what it was that he had to say to the Ghost and God and Jesus. Frank reasoned that if Mary knew that he was going to talk to Jesus tonight and if she knew what he was going to tell Him – his penance prayers addressed to her would help. His prayers were always more to Mary than to Jesus. She was always there; she had time to listen to him. He knew that Jesus was always listening as well, but he was so busy and important, *and* he was a bit frightening. Although not so intimidating as his father God, and the other one.

Frank was confident that Mary would understand, and then afterwards she would have a word with Jesus: she would ask Him not to be angry. Frank was scared by what he was doing. He could not think of a bigger sin than this. This must be the biggest ever sin. This was being cheeky to Jesus ... and his dad God, and the Ghost! Hesitantly he tried to tell them that – when he had to – he wanted to be able to die. Just die, and- die completely. He did not want to die and go to Purgatory, where he would burn for a while, where he would have to be in the flames long enough to clear his sins – before he would be allowed to go to heaven to see *them*, and live with them for always. He wanted to *BE* – and then just ... *NOT BE!*

Neither Frank nor Joe was ever certain that Mary, Jesus, or God heard or accepted their decision, and they remained uncertain of their exact status within the faith. They learned to parrot the Catechism: daily they survived Sister Alice, her ruler on the knuckles, and her pinching fingers, and they followed the prescribed path to Confirmation.

At the same time, with Father Daniel coaxing, encouraging, and occasionally bullying, they learned how to read; how to read better; how to write; write better; and how to do sums. They copied the Priest's drawing of an enormous OXO cube parked on the wing of a banking Spitfire. War was as remote and vague as a blackboard OXO – and so was Mom and Home.

Frank's infant self-pity hardened into the pragmatism of a stronger young being. He kept in the background as much as possible, increasingly focused on and coping with each day and situation as it arrived: religion, lessons, countryside, chores, friends, enemies, Brian ... Mrs Harding. Without knowing it his fear of Mrs Harding gradually altered; it became an intense dislike that he hid from her. Dislike which grew as his fear of her diminished – it grew as he managed his fear: as he endured and survived

One of the School Assistants recruited in the Village was Mary, the daughter of Edna Harding's sister, and recent witness to Frank's embarrassment and shame. She had four months to wait before she could go to the Teacher Training College in Stoke, and this job in the school was a rare opportunity for her to gain experience ahead of her course. When she first entered his class Frank was embarrassed, and she too felt uncomfortable at the recollection of that first meeting with its gratuitous nastiness. She went out of her way to catch up with him after school was over for the day.

They walked together and Mary told the embarrassed boy that she regretted being at her Aunt's house when he had been laughed at. "I'm really sorry that we had to meet like that Frank. I thought that it was cruel and unpleasant. My Mother had asked me to go, for Aunt Edna is always complaining to her that I never visit her, and she knows that I go regularly to see my Grandmother … *and* I visit another Auntie, who I am fond of in the Village. Anyway, when I got home that day I told my Mother what had happened, and I told her that I will never go to Aunt Edna's again."

Frank mumbled, "It's OK … Thanks." Although he was uncomfortable with the walk and their talk, he was happy to have her apologies for that afternoon. It meant that he did not have to fight the memory every time he saw Mary in class. In their continuing, if rather one way conversation, Mary told him, "Mom has told me that Aunt Edna is known for being unkind; Mom has fallen out with her many times over the years, and they were not happy in childhood together. Mom was very upset to hear that *you* were made unhappy there." She went on to ask him, "Can we be friends Frank?" He looked up at her face; recognised the transparent honesty in her and gave a shy smile of agreement. He had *another* friend! They became good friends within the school environment, and on the fringes of the school day.

Because he was doing so well at his lessons she was often left to coach him within a group: two girls and Frank, all of them standing so far ahead in their class at reading. Often, secretly she passed a sweet to him, and more rarely a home baked scone sent by her mother.

Shortly after Mary's arrival at the school, Frank was surprised when Mrs Hinton, the WVS lady, waylaid him after school. She asked him how he was getting on in his billet at the Harding's. Did he have any problems? Was everything alright? Was everything *normal and OK*? Frank could only grunt that everything was OK, and after his second surprised grunt he was excused further inquisition. At his age and with his limited experience of *anything*, everything in his life *was* normal. There was nothing to compare it with, so of course everything was alright. It was what his life was, and his life was normal – wasn't it?

Mary Hinton was pushed for time and for the time being she let Frank off further questioning. Mrs Hinton and Mary's mother were close friends. They were members of the Women's Institute of the Village, and the two ladies met and regularly talked together.

Chapter 13

Clarissa Graham was a leading member of the Women's Institute. The WI, popularly known as the 'Wild Indians', although labelled 'Jam and Jerusalem' by Bill Harding and others, was an active club. It monitored, and kept its inspecting nose stuck into all of the day to day happenings of the village. It was never short of an opinion, nor was it ever coy about expressing it, but its value to the community was that it rarely interfered beyond its convivial 'do good' nature.

Today Clarissa had arranged to meet Mary Hinton at the cottage that Mary shared with her mother. Mary was likely to be the next chairman of the council, and she was already chair of the institute. Perhaps her problem was not exactly institute business, but it had to be talked out with Mary anyway – she was the Evacuation Officer! Clarissa was sure that Mary would know what to do!

She could have gone to the new school in the Village Hall, but the thought of meeting that awful nun frightened her, something *needed* to be done, *had* to be done. She was *not* being silly. She hurried to be on time as arranged.

Mary was so very busy now with her evacuee job. She had confided at the Institute that what had started as a straightforward sorting-out of accommodation for the children, had turned into a full time welfare exercise, and she could not walk away from it.

On her way Clarissa gave a tiny wave of her hand to Mrs Harding, who came out of the Post Office shop as she passed. 'I have never liked that woman,' Clarissa thought, but she gave a tiny tight smile and nodded to her.

'She's a snotty cow; with her head is up her own arse,' was Edna's unkind opinion, as she smilingly waved in return.

Bill Harding had scoffed when Edna told him that she was going to join the Institute. She made pickles and jam to support her attendance for the first time, and this sparked a rare rant from her husband. "You live in a house at the wrong address," he chided her, "a house with an outside bog! You're not going to become upper class by giving jam and pickles for the 'Jam and Jerusalem' raffle." He had to make another point, "It is not as though we have too much of that stuff for ourselves."

In truth Bill was angry that with this aspiration, his wife was telling him how unhappy with her lot she had become. She wanted more than he could give her on the money that a farm labourer earned. He knew that Edna was really envious of her sister who lived in a house with a proper closet – a WC -right by her back door and connected to the village drains. *Her* husband was an 'office' man, a Buyer working at a factory in Burton. He had heard that the factory was making important bits for aeroplanes being manufactured in Birmingham. *He* wore a suit and went to work in a car. *He* was a Buyer, important and rich. Bill was a labourer, insignificant and poor.

A few minutes after her mother had answered the cottage door to Clarissa Graham, Mary Hinton arrived home. The two women sat and drank the tea which Mary's mother made for them; they talked without consequence for a while. But there was a meeting of the Parish Council this evening and Mary, with this deadline to meet, finally had to broach the subject.

"How can I help you Clarissa?" she asked. She thought that perhaps she had not been heard for Mrs Graham continued to sit in silence for a while longer. Then the tale came out in disjointed parcels of fact, conjecture and prejudice.

Susan Clements, the evacuee, was destroying her life. Her marriage was under threat from the girl.

The astonished WVS Officer remembered Susan. The image she recalled was of a very, very pretty girl, with golden hair done up in ringlets, well dressed in a cotton frock, white knee high stockings, and lovely, shiny black, patent leather shoes. She had remarked on the shoes at the time of billet allocation, and had thought then how unusually well-dressed the girl had been. She also remembered how Mrs Clarissa Graham had commandeered the girl and marched her away like a prize won.

"I think Susan is *ten*; she's *not yet eleven* is she?" she asked. Mrs Graham nodded, but qualified rather than ignored this ironic implication of a ten year old girl being able to destroy her life, by answering, "She says that she is ten – but she is more like ten going on twenty if you want my opinion!"

The story unfolded that Susan had practically taken charge of the Graham household. She was not the ornamental pretty little thing that Mrs Graham wanted around the place. After the first couple of days living at the house she ignored the little routine jobs which had been allocated to her, like helping with the washing-up; making her own bed; laying the table for meals; occasionally preparing vegetables; running errands to the shop and small tasks like that.

The chores did not sound too onerous to Mary, who remained silent letting her neighbour release all of the tensions that had been building up since the arrival in her home of the pretty Susan. "She will not *do* anything that she does not want to do. She uses the Grange like a hotel – and today Mrs Cooper gave me her notice, her immediate notice! She tells me that she is not coming any more. I don't know *exactly* how Susan has upset her, but Mrs Cooper told me very clearly that she will not work in a house where Susan is able to upset her every single day."

She elaborated, "I *do* know that *Miss Susan* returned some ironing to her – told her that she had not done it properly: it was not good enough!" With feeling she added, "The little minx!"

Mary Hinton had visited the Grange several times. It was a large and impressive Georgian house which stood to the south of the Village. It's extensive, and beautifully maintained grounds had regularly hosted the pre-war Village Fetes. Although Clarissa called Mrs Cooper her 'Daily', Mary knew that she worked full time at the house, and Mrs Cooper's husband, Bert, a retired miner, worked for most of the week in the gardens. If Clarissa had lost her 'Daily' she had undoubtedly lost her gardener as well. This was a disaster for her. The house and extensive grounds were impossible to maintain without help. How on earth could a slip of a girl inspire so much havoc in so short a time?

The answer it transpired was Edward Cooper, Clarissa's husband. It was Edward who had suggested that they should *select* an evacuee, rather than wait to have one allocated to them. They had no children of their own, and increasingly they were aware that something was missing from their lives because of this.

Over the years of their marriage the Grahams had been developing the business, from the old fashioned gentlemanly affair that Edward had taken over from his father, into the modern industrial being that it was now. It had required the total commitment of all that the couple had. In the early years of their marriage the investment was more than their money: the 'Firm' demanded all of their time, energy, enthusiasm and dreams.

There had been no place for children on their business merry-go-round. Any love, and all the energy they had was expended on their partnership – the 'Firm' and the home that they loved so much – the Grange.

Their business had grown. From being a specialist saddlers and a maker of pony traps, it was now manufacturing all sorts of carriages and small motorised vehicles, even developing a small car which they assembled from sub-contracted components and parts. The war was now bringing additional orders to the already successful company. Profitable orders on a scale which promised continuity and success greater than anything previously dreamed of.

With more and more of his time pre-empted by the demands of the firm's growth, Edward Graham had become aware and concerned about the happiness of his wife. They no longer worked together as they did when growing the company. The roles that they previously shared – accountancy, marketing and selling were now necessarily taken by the specialists they employed.

Edward reasoned that if they *had* to have an evacuee in the house then it would be best to select a young girl: this would allow them to meet their billeting obligations, and at the same time the girl could be a help and a companion for his wife. He knew that if they did not volunteer for one child they could well be lumbered with two or even more evacuees. There were plenty of spare rooms at the Grange, but there was one vacancy only for a ladies companion.

Edward delighted in Susan from their first encounter. She flattered him outrageously and charmed him with all sorts of sweet innocent attentions. Susan made a ritual of his homecoming when he returned to the Grange after each day at his factory in Burton. Escorting him to his armchair in the study she would skip off to return with his newspaper, his pipe, and his slippers. Another excursion and she would bring to his chair the silver tray with a crystal tumbler, the whisky decanter and the soda siphon.

In the early days Clarissa had been amused by these charming and childlike flatteries. Then she began to understand that this was what her husband wanted: this was what he needed from his home. It was what he did not get from his wife.

Too late she saw a beguiling young girl taking over the role that should have been hers. Edward would not listen to any criticism of the girl, he was besotted, and increasingly Susan became unmanageable. With dumb insolence she ignored any instruction from Clarissa, and did what *she* wanted to do, which was to lie late in bed, and particularly to do none of the chores set for her. She was often impertinent to Mrs Cooper, leading to today's walk out of the indispensable 'Daily'.

Mary Hinton was about to end the conversation. Increasingly aware of the passing of time, and her rapidly approaching meeting, she was finding herself more and more annoyed with this woman's inability to control a wee girl.

She was about to suggest to Clarissa that she should talk with the big nun, Sister Alice. It sounded as though young Susan was in need of some 'advice', some discipline, and some 'correction' from the nun. The Sister had publicly declared that *she* was the one in charge; she had proclaimed that she alone was responsible for the evacuees' control and welfare. Mary could not discipline Susan, and she certainly couldn't re-billet the girl – just because she was a bit of a nuisance.

Mary's intent was forestalled however when Mrs Graham spoke again. In a low defeated voice she told her companion, "I returned home earlier than expected on Saturday afternoon: I had been to visit Mrs Yerby at the hospital … Did you know she had been taken into the General? Anyway she was released unexpectedly – and of course nobody bothered to tell anyone! She was back at home even before I got to the hospital. So I was unexpectedly early when I came back here." She paused before continuing, "I came back to find Susan sitting on Edward's knee – with her arms around his neck! Would you believe it? You will understand Mary that I was very upset to see them like that … I blew up of course!"

Mary had an immediate vision of Clarissa 'blowing up', then waited for her visitor to regain her composure and continue. "Susan jumped off his knee when she saw me. She knows that it's wrong, and she *does* know what she's doing. But she has been on his lap again, and she doesn't try to hide it now. Neither of them do! It's very wrong for a young girl to do that!" Clarissa was increasingly distressed.

Mary handed her a folded handkerchief and she dabbed at her

eyes with it before going on, "It's getting worse Mary. It was funny at first – things like Edward feeding her from his plate – pudding, or something she fancied. Pathetic perhaps, but still amusing. He was just spoiling her and it didn't seem terribly wrong. Now I have again found her perched on his lap: sitting there … and he like a Cheshire cat. He has lost his reason. Her arms round his neck. Sloppy childish kisses! And he loves it!"

There was a pause as Clarissa considered this before she carried on. "I thought I knew Edward: we've been married nearly thirty years. I've never thought of him as stupid; now I find him childishly stupid. I know that he is under a lot of stress at the factory – every day there's a new and bigger problem – but that's no reason for him to go gaga. He is younger in the head than *she* is! Legs everywhere, giggling away, God knows; it's all on show: *FOR GOD'S SAKE*. Tickling each other; pretending it's a game; both of them. It isn't a game Mary … It has to be stopped before it gets out of hand. And if I can't stop it one way, then I'll stop it another!"

She startled Mary with an oath which was entirely out of character for her. Muttering through her tears she threatened, "If you don't get her away then I will! I'll swing for the manipulative little bitch!"

Mary was astonished at the revelations and told her friend so. However she was out of time, and as prospective Chairman of the Council she could *not* be late.

"I'm so sorry Clarissa but tonight I *have* to attend a Council Meeting. I'm already a little late, but I shall be clear of it by nine o'clock. Can I suggest that you stay here and then, after the meeting, we can go together to the Grange, when we can do something about the problem?"

Clarissa however decided that she would make her way home immediately; she did not want to leave her husband and Susan alone together for so long. It was agreed that Mary would drive out to the Grange after the meeting. She would be there as early as she could. Clarissa could guarantee that Susan would not be in bed until after Mary's visit, and she would make sure that her husband wasn't in bed either.

As the upset woman left for home Mary put a reassuring hand on her shoulder, and told her quietly, *"We will sort this out Clarissa.* You and I can do whatever is necessary: we'll work out something. And we will sort it ourselves, there will be no need to get that fearful nun involved!" and soberly she added, "or the Police!"

But as she walked across to the Village Hall meeting Mary thought, 'How on earth could I be so positive? Clarissa expects me to remove the girl. It *is* intolerable – but Edward is not evil, and the girl is not evil either. And importantly – however much I would like to – I cannot take Susan away from the Grange: there is no other billet available. Perhaps the only thing that I *can* do is to pass it over: put it into the hands of Sister Alice. The Nun can sort out this silly little girl.'

Chapter 14

After the Parish Council meeting had ended, Mrs Hinton collected her small car and drove to the Grange. She was dangerously short of coupons for the rest of the month, but she had to use the car, the Grange was too far away to walk, without lights, on this black night.

She hoped that she would be allowed to make a claim for extra petrol coupons to allow her to use her car for trips like this. You were allowed extra petrol for business use, and this was definitely business use.

Arriving at the Grange she was surprised to have the door opened for her by Edward Graham. With the blackout regulations demanding that no glimmer of light was to leak from a house, he had switched the entrance hall light off before opening the door for her. She was silently ushered into the small dark foyer. There when the door was closed and the light relit she was astonished by the appearance of her host.

He sported a badly puffed eye, and a smeared bloody face: the scratch marks showing red and black on his cheeks. Obviously his wife had told him that she would be visiting – and why. It seemed that the object of her visit had been dramatically aired.

Without a word, the tall and unusually chastened owner of the Grange led her into the Drawing room; a recently kicked shin obliged him to walk with a limp. His wife Clarissa was waiting for them there. And the amazed Mary Hinton saw that Susan was there too.

Mrs Graham was sitting on one of the splendid Bergere settees: Mary had admired these on previous visits to the Grange. She was nursing a cut glass tumbler of whisky and she cheerily greeted Mary, "Good Heaven Mary! You must have punctured some of the gas-bags on the Council tonight. You are much earlier than I expected."

She looked across at her husband who remained standing by the door, and chided him, "Do get Mary Hinton a drink Edward!" Then turning to and addressing the open mouthed Mrs Hinton, "Would it be a whisky and soda Mary?" She rambled on, "I'm afraid we're out of gin. But we do have some cognac, and I think we can show off with some sherry, if you would prefer it? It's all from under the counter now isn't it? Or from someone, who knows *someone*, on the Black Market. Lack of our wee welcome home drink in the evening is going to be one of the more painful sacrifices from the war I think."

Dumbfounded, and still not having said a word since she had arrived, Mary accepted the whisky and soda that Edward Graham had poured for her. Not waiting for her to make up her mind he had taken the 'which drink' decision for her.

Mary had been stunned into her silence as a reaction to the scene before her, and she remained silent as she watched Clarissa Graham sipping at her drink, for Clarissa was sitting, and sitting very solidly, on the lap of a wide eyed Susan Clements.

At last, as though sensing that there needed to be an explanation for her position, Clarissa rose and moved. She shepherded Mary Hinton to the second matching settee, where they sat together. Susan remained where she sat, looking a little embarrassed, and a trifle flat.

"We three have been discussing certain things: matters that very much had to be discussed," laughingly explained Clarissa as they settled on the settee with their drinks. Simultaneously they sipped, Clarissa savouring the whisky with obvious relish, while Mary, with her eyes down and with hesitant sipping, avoided conversation. They regarded Susan who remained passively in her seat, while silently regarding them in return.

Clarissa related, "Susan, Edward, and I have enjoyed a long chat. I think – no, I *know* – that our chat has been very worthwhile, and I do believe that we have straightened out a lot of things and we have answered a lot of questions."

She turned to Mary and laughed, "You must have found that very funny: Susan and I sitting together like that!" Mary raised her eyebrows and gave a slight nod in agreement as Clarissa continued, "I was making a point to Susan: that it can appear peculiar to anyone seeing it. It is absurd – sitting on someone's lap." She paused, turning to face Susan. "I think that we have agreed … haven't we Susan? That it is a thing that children do, they can do it naturally, but adults can only do it in an artificial way. So they don't do it." She rose, and moved back to sit next to Susan on the other settee.

Taking the girl's hand she held it in both of hers. Gently and quietly she spoke directly – to the girl alone. "We *can* be friends Susan, and we *must* be friends if we are to share our home together. I have seen a spirit; I recognise the individuality, in you. It's something that I would not want to stifle. I do not want to change you, but we all have to conform to certain standards of behaviour. On my part I must respect you, and I do. And I want to enjoy your presence here – as *a friend* – *not* as a lovely ornamental trophy doll. I would like us to start again. I *want* you to stay with us: I very much want you to stay here, and I know that we can *all* be happy," looking towards the door and at Edward standing immobile there. "But there cannot be any silly games … and that applies to us all … including me."

There was an unusual mistiness in Susan's eyes as she raised her head towards Clarissa; after a long reflection she nodded dumbly. Clarissa folded her into her arms, and very quietly they shared a few tears. Mary too enjoyed a little weep.

Clarissa helped Susan and they stood up together. When Clarissa spoke again she was still holding her by her shoulders.

"Go and run a bath for yourself, dear Susan. You must be exhausted. Have a long soak – use the scented green salts that are in the wall cupboard: they are lovely … very relaxing. I will bring a hot drink up to you when you get into bed. It's been a long and awkward day – for all of us; tomorrow will be so much better!"

When Susan had left the room Clarissa freshened Mary's glass and her own before speaking to her husband, "Can I get *you* a drink darling? Mary and I need to talk – and it's not men-talk, so – would you like us to go into the study, or will you go there?" Her husband mumbled that he was 'on his way'.

As he poured his drink his wife moved to him and quietly but clearly said, "I am so sorry about what happened today Edward. But we could not live in the pantomime that our marriage was becoming. I don't regret anything that I have said tonight – but I do regret that something *had* to be said. I am really sorry for any hurt that I have caused you, but believe me darling I am sharing that hurt. I love you so very much Edward. We have to be partners for ever – and we can be now. Please say that everything is back to normal now," she corrected herself. "No! Everything is *better than normal* now!"   Edward patted her backside as agreement. He left the room with his filled glass, carrying the decanter. He nodded and smiled at Mary as he left.

Mary was amazed at the different Clarissa she had met tonight. She was strong; she was genuine: she was a surprise. Mary learned that the catalytic change had *not* been when Clarissa decided to sit upon Susan. Much had been already resolved by that time, and that action had truly been a demonstration: her way of showing the girl that sitting on his lap was a ridiculous way of coercing advantage from a silly man, when there were much better and less dangerous methods, of getting puddings and favours and advantages in life.

The turning point had come with the realisation by Clarissa and Susan that they could talk honestly together, and their discovery that they needed to talk, and more importantly, they wanted to talk.

After taking the hot chocolate drink to Susan: the drink that she had promised earlier, and having settled the girl, luxuriously comfortable and snoozily happy in her bed, Clarissa returned to join her friend in the sitting room.

They talked for a long time; long enough indeed for them to have need in the late evening to rescue the decanter from the study. Clarissa related all the events of the day, beginning with Edward's return from the factory. To start it all off there had been an almighty row! Mary had seen the evidence of that in Edward's face and limp.

But then Clarissa admitted that she had found it impossible to take the row further and involve Susan in it. She could not brawl with the young girl, the worldly girl who, under that veneer of sophistication, was actually a ten year old child.

She learned that Susan did not know her own father: she did not know who her father was. If she had met him at some time she did not remember the meeting. She *had* known many 'uncles'. And she remembered a recent incumbent with particular fondness. She saw her mother infrequently, but was proudly aware that she was an actress working in London. She had been in a film – but Susan hadn't seen it and didn't know its title. However her mother supported her by sending money regularly to the people who successively had looked after her daughter.

For the past several months Susan had lived with an elderly couple at their home on the outskirts of Birmingham. Before that there had been a different 'Auntie' and another 'Uncle' with whom she had lived. She told Clarissa that she was very sad when Auntie Mabel had to go into hospital. Without his wife Uncle Dennis could not look after the girl. That had been just before the war started.

Evacuation solved the problem. The war began; evacuation happened, and evacuation took Susan and the problem away.

"That's what she called it Mary – *the problem!* She sees herself as an undeserved problem for her mother. Susan thinks of her mother with pride and love, but – without meeting her – I can truly hate that woman. She has casually passed on her own values, or lack of values, to her daughter. Her living style is the example she gave to Susan. She has shown her that by flirting she can get what she wants from men. From *uncles*," Clarissa declared indignantly.

The two women talked into the night. They discussed the situation: Susan, evacuation, the war. As the decanter was emptied they conspired and developed a plan of action. The obvious and immediate solution to the problem was to hand over the responsibility for Susan to the Catholic school. Clarissa emphatically vetoed that option.

"That is not an option!" she ranted. "There is no way that Susan is going to be thought of as a problem to be handled by that … *woman*," she went on indignantly. "Susan is an intelligent girl. She wants to stay with us and that's OK. We have all agreed that. She may think that rules are being applied for her specially, but she will soon understand that there aren't any rules really – only the conventions that we all have to live by. She has told me that there is a trunk of her belongings which is still being held by the last couple she lived with, and I am sending for that tomorrow."

She checked the level of her companion's glass before continuing, "Susan was so happy when I told her that I was sending for her trunk and with a little luck she should have her things by the weekend. She loves her clothes. She says that her mother is always sending her presents. It's mainly clothes that she sends. I am going to help her write to her mother tomorrow. She has the current address – and although Susan isn't too sure about writing – it is only because she really does see herself as *the problem*."

Mary Hinton agreed with her friend that it *was* important to write. It would be nice if they found out if there was love there. Love as well as pretty frocks and expensive, shiny black shoes.

When Mary, enjoying an unusual glow, eventually left the Grange, she left an acquaintance who had become a friend. A newly recognised friend, and – glory be – who had become a volunteer! For Clarissa had committed herself to helping Mary with the task of evacuee welfare. She claimed that she had volunteered without any help from her whisky.

"I've been far too self-indulgent for far too long," she told Mary. "I can help you. I know that I can do a job, and I would love to. And Susan will work with me. We will work together to help. From what you have told me she isn't the only child who is – or who thinks she is – a problem. Kids should not have to suffer such nonsense. And within our comfortable complacency we do not really know just what they are going through. All children are so very worthwhile aren't they?"

Chapter 15

In Birmingham, Frank's mother Gladys Bourne was facing another crisis – and just as she was getting straight!

She was on piece-work now at Albrights: collecting regular wages, two pounds ten shillings, and more each week: good wages getting better as her technique for handling the heavy components improved. With increasing speed on the lathe she was turning out more and more 4" shell castings to the tight tolerance required. Now, with every completed shell she removed from the lathe bed, as she manhandled it into the out-pallet, Gladys mentally added the piece-price to the wage packet she would get on Saturday.

Now, upsetting the apple cart, her mother was being bloody minded about the kids. She would have Joan, but Charlie had to leave. He was due to leave school, but instead of going into a factory he had made up his mind to join the Navy. He would be leaving anyway. He was going away, and the prospect of a wage was going with him. So he could bloody well sod off now.

A wage packet would have been wonderful for Granny Jenkins: she needed it and keenly felt the injustice of his decision to leave, just when he could repay something for the years that she had fostered him.   She had fallen out with the boy and in her bloody minded anger one day she locked *the ungrateful little sod* out of the house. Instead of seeking refuge by going to Pretoria Court to face the wrath of his mother, he had wandered out to Castle Bromwich, and that night he had slept out in the bluebell wood behind the ancient Hall. It had been a long and uncomfortable night; with his discomfort and his round-and-round thoughts, little sleep had been possible.

In the early hours of the chilly morning, the dawn that he had been waiting and marking time for, Charlie surfaced from his non-sleep and stirred warmth into his body. He eased his bladder, and shook, scratched and brushed himself into respectability.

The boy's plan – he reasoned that it was the first plan he had made in his life – was simple, and it started with the long walk into the City. Purposefully he walked past, through and around all the evidence of an industrial City at War, and under siege.

In order to get warm and keep warm, he walked briskly and arrived at the recruiting office in Martineau Street well ahead of time. Feeling conspicuously out of place, Charlie was surrounded by the fully awake early morning routine of the industrial city. Noisy trams dominated the scene. Impressive and friendly double deck trams. He watched them as they impatiently filled. Once their bellies were stuffed he watched the familiar yellow beasts trundling away, very often with a double clang notice of departure on the foot bell. This was the terminus, at rush hour, and the departing tram was quickly replaced by another. Another cargo of Woodbine smoking workers – in grey macs with lunch packed pockets – were soon on their way. He did not belong there, did not belong anywhere – yet. He walked into the recruiting office as it opened, glad to leave the scene.

The pensioned Petty Officer veteran welcomed him as his first customer. He saw a likely lad, and in the lull before the busy day got under way he gave the dishevelled, rather grubby youth a mug of sweet tea. Gratefully nursing the hot mug, Charlie was told that the Navy was a wonderful life.

"Compare fresh air and freedom with a factory. Compare having a go at the Nazis – with sitting in a factory waiting for them to call with a bomb." he was advised. And the early start he would be making, as a Boy Seaman, was the best apprenticeship for the wonderful life.

Because of his age he would need his Mom to sign an agreement. Would she sign? Charlie was certain that she would!

The Doctor arrived shortly after the tea was finished. There and then Charlie was measured and examined; every bit of him was poked, prodded, and assessed, before the Doctor confirmed that he was fit enough to join the Navy and join the War.

The first that the startled Gladys knew of this was when another rare letter arrived at Pretoria Court. It invited her to sign for and authorise Charlie Bourne's entry into the Royal Navy. With her signature he would be enrolled as a Boy Seaman, and within two weeks he would enter a shore training establishment called H.M.S. Ganges. This was at Harwich in Suffolk – wherever that was.

At the end of her day's work she went to see him at her mother's house in Saltley. It wasn't an easy walk. She was diverted from the normal route several times. Demolition of buildings and clear up work was going on everywhere. Houses and shops made unsafe by the bombing of recent days were being pulled down into piles of still smoking rubble.

There had been a raid the night before, not a big one, the alarm sounding at 7 o'clock just as she reached home. There was no shelter at home, partly because there was no room for a corrugated iron Anderson in a back-to-back house that had no garden. And the Council's stock of Anderson shelters had run out anyway. Gladys was exhausted from her day's work, and when the alarm siren had sounded she had thought about staying in the house. In a previous raid she had dragged the sturdy deal table up to the angle of the stairs, and had curled up under the dubious shelter that the stairs and the upended table provided. The wrecked houses she passed today confirmed that shelter in them wasn't an option. So the early part of last night had been spent in the crowded, damp and claustrophobic Deep Shelter by Aston Cross.

The raids were a long time coming after War had been declared, and there had been complacency about the threat. There was no complacency now. That had evaporated over many evening and night bombing raids which followed the City's first calm year of the War.

The raids culminated just over a month ago – with the big one. Gladys would remember for ever the fruumm … fruumm … fruumm sound – so easily construed, and heard as – 'for…brum … For…brum'. It was the noise of heavily loaded bomber engines – and the hate and the fury which they brought with them. They said that nearly three hundred German bombers had concentrated their venom on Birmingham that night. Thousands had died; many incinerated.

Miraculously the City shook itself and recovered after each raid. The water and gas mains were reinstated; the electricity supplies were re-run and reconnected; the wrecked buildings demolished; the roads cleared, and even the trams kept running, albeit on a restricted basis. Many of the factories were hit and many destroyed, but they kept producing what the War demanded, and Gladys had not missed a single shift at Albrights. But everybody living here knew that they lived close to, very close to, the gas works; the power station; the railway goods yard; B.S.A.; Fort Dunlop; Moss Gear; and the Nuffield factories: all of them prime targets for Hitler's bombers.

When she arrived at her mother's house Gladys was tired and suffering from a deep headache. She was already thinking of the long walk home, and of the limited time she had before the alarms would sound again.

It was not a pleasant meeting. Charlie stayed in the yard cleaning his boots and looking as innocent as he could. Joan was out doing errands. She was delivering some completed washing. Hopefully she would be bringing more bundles home for her Gran to work on.

"About time you took an interest in your kids," was the surly greeting Gladys received from her mother. "Its weeks since you came. And I don't suppose you've brought any grocery money now either." Gladys didn't correct her mother, but it was less than a week since her last visit. She handed some cash to her and the formidable woman was a little less belligerent as she grumbled on.

It was the same, familiar moaning: fewer families could afford to have their washing done for them; the water was forever being cut off; and there was no other way for her to earn money. And she had to work and earn money ... Just to keep her daughter's kids! She was too old for working 'back of Lewis's'. She had been relying on Charlie going to work, and bringing a bit in, it wasn't much to ask. But he had to run off – just like his Father!

Gladys could see that there was no way out of this endless grumbling with its barbarously painful comments and accusations.

When she called Charlie into the house he emphatically confirmed that he knew what he was doing. He wanted to go. She licked the point of the stub end indelible pencil she carried in her bag, and signed for Charlie's escape to the War. She handed the document to her son without a word, and left with him. They didn't wait for the return of her daughter Joan.

Charlie walked with his Mother until their routes parted at Cato Street by the Saltley Gas Works. He carried on the walk to Town. He was delivering the authorisation by hand, anxious to get involved before the War ended. When he pushed the re-used envelope through the door of the now closed recruiting office he was thinking of his brother Dave, who was already *in* the Royal Navy. Dave was out of this bloody place – Brum.

In the following months Charlie never debated the decision he had taken: it was something 'done and dusted': *he was IN*. He was a Boy Seaman at the shore training establishment HMS Ganges.

Although on occasion he was to think ruefully about the high wages his contemporaries were earning in the Birmingham factories, he adapted quickly to the inflexibly tough, almost brutal training regime that he had entered.

The indoctrination and training period over several months

was exhausting. Months when you never walked, but moved everywhere at the double march: fists clenched, forearms parallel to the ground, back rigidly upright and boots pounding at 180 paces to the minute. You were taught how to march. You were taught the Slow, the Quick, and the Double march. In practice thereafter though it was never at the Slow and rarely at the Quick – it was always at the Double.

You were introduced to the novelty of the shower, and the even bigger novelty of the *daily* shower. You were taught how to shower; how properly to clean teeth, and how to wash clothes.

You were taught how to sling your hammock – its width restricted to 18 inches by a wooden stretcher bar hooked into its head. You learned how to sling it, and how to get in and out of it, suspended as it was from the hooks and rails mounted six feet above the mess deck. Swinging and clambering, in and out of the hammock, and sleeping within your eighteen inches wide allowance in a sea of hammocks. Taught how to lash your canvas bed and bedding into a regulation tight sausage, and how to stow it in the hammock netting storage. How to bed down as Nelson's men did – afloat and ashore.

All boy seamen during training were exercised, mainly at the double of course; they were injected, verbally abused, vaccinated, bullied some more, occasionally clouted, and generally re-shaped. Sitting in regulation posture their heads were shorn to regulation anonymity.

His mate, his oppo, commented to Charlie, "We're bleeding lucky they haven't worked out how to get us all down to a regulation height."

Regularly with the others Charlie presented his kit for inspection. As the boys did this they knew that their new possessions, so precisely laid out to formula on their spare canvas hammock, would *never* satisfy the Petty Officer, or the Divisional Officer. It was always imperfect. Inevitably they would be chastised for a poor showing with additional doubling around the parade ground: maintaining and gasping at the regulation 180 paces per minute, and often – for some actual or perceived breach of discipline – carrying and suffering under the half-hundredweight of a shell.

Daily you were awakened before dawn to the reveille of a raucous bugle being played on the parade ground. You were often up ended out of your hammock by a Bosun's Mate ducking under the lines of sleep-hungry boys, and repeatedly screaming, "WAKEY-WAKEY-WAKEY – Lash up and stow! Rise and shine. The morning's fine! AND you've had your time." Often commenting more close to the truth, "It's pissing down!" And frequently improvising shocking wake-up banter; perhaps subtly suggesting, "Hands OFF off off Cocks – ON on on Socks," before less subtly adding, "You Tossers!"

Another day to survive; a mad timetable of physical and Parade training to endure; more 'schooling' to suffer; introduction to seamanship, and signals, and sailing: to learn, master and enjoy. Beginning to understand the standards required by the Service: standards of conformity, cleanliness and above all the discipline: unquestioning obedience. Everything became easier with practice, easier by being shared, and easier still by achievement.

The entire intake was of like background. They were entering a career the hard way, the casual unplanned way of the working class. Friendships were forged, enmities exposed, frequent scraps breaking out in the mess huts, to be quickly settled, and merged into the day's routine.

But within the gruelling day were the highlights brought about by FOOD! The Boy Seamen, to a man, had never experienced the luxury of so much manna. There was BREAKFAST; there was DINNER; there was TEA, and there was SUPPER. Wonderful food with soups and puddings! Substantial helpings of good quality well cooked food. Big white platefuls of the stuff, with as much bread and margarine and mugs of sweet tea as you could manage.

The work became manageable, and yet more manageable, with

the approach of each happily predictable next meal. Even the Mast became less daunting to the newly well-fed developing urchins from industrial Britain.

The Mast was essentially a Man of War's mainmast, incorporating various wooden and metal spars from other warships which had served in the days of sail. It towered some one hundred and fifty feet above the Parade Ground, and the Boy Seamen were required to 'man' it as part of their discipline and character training. It was a key item in ceremonial parades, and a looming accompaniment to every single day they spent at Ganges. Charlie and his Mates were scared at the sight of the notorious mast and terrified the first time that they were ordered to man it.

Manning the mast involved all of the boys rhythmically climbing and lining the shrouds and yards of the mast right up to the Button at the masthead, with each step paced by a single drum beat. The lightning conductor at the very top – surmounting the twelve inch diameter Button – provided a single and precarious knee hold for the selected Button Boy. He stood erect and snapped into a salute when a signal from the drum told him that all of the yards and shrouds were uniformly filled with the cadets: each boy on the shrouds with one foot on a ratline; holding on with one hand while the other arm star-fished out into space.

Charlie became a successful Upper Yards man, but he happily avoided the Button Boy honour in his months at Ganges. He did however wonder if his mother would be proud to see him like that.

All the Boy Seamen were encouraged by the Navy to write home, and Charlie carefully penned a short letter to his mom. He told her that he was doing great at seamanship; that he especially enjoyed sailing, and he was above average in the continuing school lessons that the Navy insisted on. He also told her without rancour, that her rather casual signature, in indelible pencil, together with his own signing had committed him to *fifteen* years in the Navy. He had been told that very day that the normal twelve year contract that they had committed to would not *start* until he was eighteen years old. But never mind!

Needing to tell someone else about his new life and success he asked his mother for Little Frank's address. He had already written to his brother Dave. Charlie hoped that when he had finished training at Ganges he could join up with him on the same ship.

Dave was in H.M.S. Hood. It was May 1941.

Chapter 16

Mary Hinton, her confidence bolstered by the WVS uniform she was wearing, walked through the village. She exchanged greetings with villagers whom she met on her purposeful passage. Everybody knew her and she enjoyed the familiarity. She had debated with herself about the uniform – should she wear it, or should she dress in her normal fashion? No, she was on duty and it should look like that. She would be official, she wasn't visiting for a chat.

Not that she had ever before visited Mr Evans, or his parents. She had called for petrol, but never for a chat.

The Evans lived at Bunford Cottage at the end of the village. When called on they operated the village's single petrol pump which was sited at the front of their ramshackle garage-workshop at the side of the house. The property, the last at this end of the village, was an uncared for mess and contrasted badly with the other well maintained village cottages. No fresh paintwork, sparkling windows or well-tended garden here, but rusting parts of discarded farm machinery and broken down and cannibalised vans and cars. Altogether they made an ugly clutter, competing with weeds and grass in the area between and around the garage and house. The wheels and tyres, glass, iron and steel showed that when something was discarded by the Evans men it stayed on the spot on which it landed when thrown.

Eric Evans and his father George were in the workshop. They were hammering at a large rusted piece of farm equipment and didn't hear Mary Hinton's arrival.

"Good afternoon Mr Evans." Her warning cough had been unheard, and they were startled when she loudly announced her presence.

"Mrs Hinton!" answered Eric, dropping the heavy maul he had been using, and wiping his hands on his trousers as he turned. He was a short wiry man in his mid-fifties. His chin was unshaven and his grey hair was dirty. Braces supported his greasy trousers over a grubby shirt and a woollen pullover of an unknown colour. His more heavily built father stood behind him.

George Evans gave the impression of past power and strength rapidly going to fat. She acknowledged him separately, "Good afternoon Mr Evans," receiving a grunt and a short nod in return.

"You want something Mrs Hinton?" asked Eric.

She answered him with her own question, "Where's Betty Mr Evans?"

"Don't know … Could be in the house, I suppose."

"I need to see her." Eric looked at his father before answering, "Come back after tea. You can see her then."

"No!" She replied crisply. "I must see her now."

"Well … It ain't actually very handy for us to leave this and go looking for her."

`"Never mind," she said, "I will go and I'll find her myself." She turned and Eric moved quickly in front of her, "Alright then. Dad will have to work on his own," he grumbled, "but it ain't convenient all the same."

Together they walked across to the gloomy looking house. Eric opened the door and entered, turning to suggest that Mrs Hinton should wait outside. She ignored his suggestion. "I need to see Betty in the house Mr Evans. I need to see her *now*… on her own … And I would like to see her in her room."

He answered her angrily, "Don't know about that!" But grudgingly he made way for her entry, calling loudly as he did so, "It's me, Ma!" There was no acknowledgement that they could hear of this call. Clearly he had not expected a response but he called loudly to add, "With a woman from the Hall – to see Betty!"

The cottage interior was even more depressing than the outside. The first room they entered was the scullery. A deeply stained sink was fitted under the small side window with, at its side a small roughly made wooden table. One corner of this room was formed by a brick built boiler, dead ashes from its last use spilling from the fire hole at its base. Mrs Hinton noted a single brass water tap fixed above the deep Belfast sink: not all village houses had a water supply piped into the house.

From the scullery they entered the main living area. Two dirty windows with grubby curtaining allowing only a little light to struggle through. The smoke stained walls hadn't seen whitewash for many years. A large table standing in the middle of the room was spread with old newspapers. It was littered with remnants of past meals: food stained plates, mugs, and cutlery. Competing for space on the table were bits and pieces of oily components brought in from the garage and waiting attention. Three unmatched upright wooden chairs at the table, a sagging armchair, and a one sided sofa to the side of the blackened cast iron cooking range completed the furniture. The range was overflowing with ashes from earlier fires: it was unlit today. There was no floor covering over the cracked and dirty quarry floor – but everywhere the debris and squalor of an uncaring bachelor's hovel.

"Stay here!" ordered Eric Evans. She wasn't inclined to move – or touch anything – as he turned into the corner stairs and clumped up the bare wooden treads.

Then Mary Hinton *did* move, for she heard the surreptitious movement of a bolt being eased. "Is Betty there?" She called in a panic from the bottom of the stairs, adding in horror, "Has she been locked in?"

"No she ain't … Course she ain't," he shouted before growling, "Come on wench … There's some nosey woman here just *has* to

104

see you. Put this on ... And come down stairs ... Move yourself now!"

Betty Frome followed Eric Evans. She walked carefully down the stairs, into the cold dark room where Mary Hinton nervously waited. "Are you alright Betty?" she asked anxiously, moving to Betty and offering a reassuring hand to the girl.

Betty slowly nodded. She didn't take the hand; she didn't look up, she didn't look at either of the two grown-ups. Mrs Hinton continued, with obvious concern in her voice, "I'm Mary." She leaned forward, bending to look up so she could see Betty's face, and went on, "We saw each other the other day ... When you first came here to Roslington. Do you remember?"

Receiving no reply she spoke to Eric Evans, who was standing close behind Betty, and shuffling from foot to foot. "Would you leave us for a few minutes ... please Mr Evans?"

"Can't do that," he grumbled, looking round the room as though counting and protecting his possessions. "It ain't right!"

"Mr Evans," she countered angrily, but with a tightly controlled conciliatory smile, "I won't be very long ... And it *is* better for us to talk in *here* rather than outside on your path. And it will be quicker – I do know that you are *very* busy and you do need to get on with your work!"

"I *am* busy," he growled, before accepting defeat and stumping off. "Don't be long ... I'll be in the garage."

Mrs Hinton didn't want to sit down in this unhappy grubby room, so remained standing as she again asked the girl, "Are you alright?"

Patiently she waited several moments before repeating, "Betty ... Are you alright? What has happened?"

Finally the girl stood erect. Without looking at the WVS lady she quietly answered, "I'm alright." She was wearing a shapeless cotton dress that came down to her bare feet. With her hands across her chest she stared at the room as though looking for some particular thing amongst the mess.

Mary took a decision. "Get properly dressed Betty: dressed to go out. Where is your coat and where are your shoes? We're going to get a cup of tea … And I want you to see Father Daniels. He's worried because you have missed school … He wants to know that you're alright. We all want to know that you are alright."

Later, after dispiritedly collecting her clothes from upstairs and from the cupboard under the corner stairs, Betty was dressed to go, and Mrs Hinton called up the stairs, "Betty is going to the school with me now Mrs Evans." Receiving a dismissive grunt Mary took the girl's arm, and they left.

The Evans men: father and son, watched as they left. Mary Hinton did not acknowledge their presence. However she could get no response from the girl to any of the questions she raised as they walked to the Village Hall.

Arriving there – now the All Saints Roman Catholic School –

She told Sister Alice that she needed to speak with Father Daniel. The nun put her down without consideration. Mary was frostily told that she couldn't talk with the priest – he was unavailable for the afternoon.

The nun looked accusingly at Betty and told Mrs Hinton that she, Sister Alice, was responsible for the evacuees in the village.
"What have you done?" the Sister demanded of Betty, staring aggressively at the downcast silent girl.

"Nothing!" Mrs Hinton angrily retorted, and she repeated, "Nothing! She has done nothing at all wrong. I need to talk with someone in authority about the billet that she is in. I would like to discuss this matter with Father Daniel. When will he be able to see me?"

The nun gave a dismissive and almost imperceptible shrug, and Mrs Hinton, with contained anger demanded, "If you *are* the person I have to talk to … Is it at all possible that you could listen to what I have to say?"

The nun gestured that they should go into a side room off the main hall in which she had been teaching. "Carry on reading the chapter four!" she commanded the children as they walked through the silent class. "There will be a test when I return. And, while I am out of this room there will be absolute silence from you! Or there will be trouble – for all of you!"

She grudgingly invited Mrs Hinton to take a seat opposite her in the small room that was serving as the school office. Betty remained standing as the WVS officer explained why she was there.

"As you are aware, Sister, I am the Billeting Officer here. As part of my job I have been checking on how the emergency billeting is working out. You know how the initial allocation of rooms became rather chaotic when you arrived the other day. We are not entirely happy that all is as good as it could be. And we cannot expect all the placements to be perfect."

Sister Alice murmured, "Very little in this sinful world is perfect." Mary ignored this and went on, "I heard today that Betty here has not been at school – at all. Did you know this Sister?" There was no reply from the nun and Mary continued, "I called today at Bunford Garage to find out why. I visited there to see if she was ill."

She was interrupted by the Sister who, turning to Betty, asked her sharply, "*Are* you ill girl?" She was answered with a silently shaken head. "Why didn't you attend classes – as you were clearly instructed to?" She warmed to her rant, continuing before the outraged Mrs Hinton could say a word in protest. "We are very short staffed here. We cannot be expected to roam through the county looking for truants."

Mary Hinton was at last able to break in. She angrily complained, "Betty is *not* ill. Well, I don't think she is … But, after the call I made today at the Bunford Cottage I do not think it is at all suitable for Betty to stay there. It is not suitable for *any* child to stay there." She broke off and moved a little away from where the forlorn, downcast Betty was standing. Sister Alice moved after her. With anger still evident in her attitude and voice, Mary spoke more quietly as she went on, "Unfortunately though, we don't have any other rooms immediately available. It will be a little time before I could organise a new billet."

She looked directly at Sister Alice, but the nun would not allow eye to eye contact; Mrs Hinton had to address her question to her averted head. "Can *you* suggest a solution Sister Alice?" She pleaded, "There *must* be a re-allocation. In my opinion it is desperately urgent."

Sister Alice did not respond, but stood up and sniffed that she had to attend to her class. She practically marched her visitor back into the entrance hallway complaining as she did so, "In *my* opinion there are very *many* children requiring attention. And special attention too."

She loudly asserted, "I am the one responsible in this case. Mine is the sole responsibility: the children were given by their parents into the care of the Church. That is specifically into *my* care. It is a sacred trust Mrs Hinton … Yes, you have my assurance that I will see to it … Yes, myself … Yes … immediately!"

Mrs Hinton was dismissed. Unhappily she was obliged to desert the forlorn Betty, who was now standing alone in the tiny office, waiting nervously for the return of Sister Alice.

For nearly an hour Betty stood in the same spot. Then, when she had to move, it was to sit on a tiny, infant sized chair that stood partly hidden behind the open door. She was exhausted: desperately unhappy, desperately alone, and wanting to be anonymous in her misery.

Betty stood up, quickly and guiltily when Sister Alice finally returned.

"I knew you would be trouble Betty Frome," the nun hissed and then added, as though she was explaining everything, "I knew your mother!" Turning out of the room she ordered, "Follow me. And hold your shoulders back. At the very least look as if there could be *some* pride in you!"

It was the end of the school day and the boys, released from the afternoon's torpor were reacting in the usual noisy and physical way of all young escapees. The girls were no less noisy. But all of them when they saw Sister Alice, or sensed her presence, fell silent and cleared a wide path for her, allowing her unimpeded passage through the corridor, the open doors and the playground; with Betty struggling to keep up in her wake. The sad girl was shamefully aware of the inspection and the bewilderment of her peers.

The ill-matched pair: the nun in her black gowned authority and the subdued pathetic girl did not take the short cut directly across the Green. They followed the longer paved route around it. Their walk took them up to and through the gates of Roslington Church – the Church of England. Continuing via the graveyard pathway they walked up to the rectory. Arriving at the porch the nun took firm hold of Betty's shoulder and pushed the unresisting girl squarely into position facing the door of the house. Sister Alice rang the bell and clattered the lions head knocker for additional effect.

Reverend Humphries opened the door promptly. He had watched their approach and was expecting them.

"Good afternoon Reverend Humphries," Sister Alice greeted him respectfully. "Thank you for kindly allowing this visit, and so immediately after our telephone conversation." Betty, who had known and suffered the nun for a long time, was astonished by the change in her. Sister Alice was fawning.

"Come inside," was the Vicar's terse response. He looked outside, peering into the approaching evening, searching the churchyard for sign of anyone witnessing this unusual and unwelcome visitation. Closing the door he led them into his living room and there, by moving his head and waving a casual hand, he invited the Sister to sit on an armchair set in the window alcove. He sat in a similar chair facing her. Betty Frome remained standing.

"Perhaps you can explain this in more detail than you gave me on the telephone," he invited brusquely. "I am *not* getting involved in the welfare, or the supervision of the *adolescents* that you have brought to this parish." *Adolescents* sounded quite like an imported infectious disease: he was smugly satisfied with that.

"No Reverend, that responsibility remains with me. In any case – having met and spoken with you – I know that you have your own heavy responsibilities caring for your own flock," was her mollifying reply. She continued in the same conciliatory way, "But this affects us both." She glanced towards Betty, the look implying that the problem was the girl. "She has been living with Mr and Mrs Evans and their son Eric at the garage house. They are of your Church I think," She sniffed before continuing, "as is a Mrs Hinton of the WVS. It is Mrs Hinton who has brought this all to a head!"

Henry Humphries was looking less self-assured and less comfortable as he heard mention of the Evans family. Being rather overweight it was normal and easy for him to perspire: his florid face glistened with sweat now.

Without waiting for his acknowledgement of these parishioners, the nun gestured towards Betty and continued, "Today Mrs Hinton brought *this* to me, saying that the Evans house is not a suitable billet for her." She looked accusingly at Betty and continued indignantly. "Not suitable even for someone in need of shelter and food, as this youth is!" Addressing the vicar she challenged him. "Would you say, indeed would you think that the Evans family are unsuitable guardians, Reverend?"

The vicar did not answer immediately, but was silent for a time, before turning and addressing Betty for the first time. His voice was not raised, and his tone was not unkindly when he asked her, "Are you complaining young lady?" She returned his stare with a blank, but not sullen, expression. The question was unanswered. "Have you anything to complain about?" Again the girl was silent. Sister Alice rose threateningly, but the Vicar stopped her with a raised open palm.

He asked another question of Betty: "Has anything happened?" And he repeated seriously, "Has anything happened to you at the Evans's house?" He carried on with his quiet, persistent inquisition, "Have you been beaten ... Have you been hit?"

At last Betty spoke, quietly answering, "No. I haven't been hit." Reverend Humphries looked at Sister Agnes, who shook her head: the resigned gesture suggesting that this was all a waste of everyone's time.

The vicar asked a final question. "Have you been ... shall we say, *hurt*?" He repeated the question "In any way have you been hurt?"

Her head remained lowered, but Betty seemed to be considering the question. She remained silent for a long time. The vicar waited and watched; the nun impatiently fingered her rosary beads. Betty, still looking at the polished wooden floor, slowly shook her head.

The vicar thought for a second or so, before he took a decision. He addressed Sister Alice. "I think we should visit the Evan's. If you do not disagree I will go with you." He went on, "Mrs Evans is bed-ridden I do believe, and I'm sure that will account for any messy untidiness in the cottage that Mrs Hinton speaks of. I have been acquainted with both men for a very long time. They do not attend church regularly, but otherwise," he paused, "I can see no obvious reason for Hinton to be so high handed!"

With this course of action decided the black-garbed nun rose and moved swiftly to the frightened girl standing by the door. She shook the flinching Betty and spitted, "You had better hope that the family who were looking after you will accept you *back* into their home Betty Frome. You had better understand that we are visitors here."

The vicar was ready to leave. He stood by the half opened door, but the nun continued with her spiteful diatribe, "Frome, you should be ashamed to behave as you have done: no humility, but that is no surprise. There is not one ounce of grace or humility in *any* of your family. Be thankful that you have been given shelter here – and remember just who you are. ... How dare you presume to compare this with your slum – and your slum family – in Birmingham?" The vicar interrupted, "Come now Sister," he murmured, "Let us get the task sorted."

Betty surreptitiously wiped her eyes, as she walked through the village behind the two God fearing zealots. They walked at the brisk pace set by the vicar, finally picking their way across the rusting scrap-strewn and neglected garden of Bunford Cottage.

Hardly formed images of an enormous web with lurking giant spiders came unbidden into Betty's head.

Chapter 17

Harry and Joe were walking down Pit Lane. School had finished for the day and the boys were walking – with no particular destination in mind – just walking away from the School. Harry had two hours free before he had to be back at the Farm for the evening milking, and Joe was free, as he always was.

Stopping to lean on the five barred gate of the pit pony field, they saw immediately that there were no ponies in the field today for them to discuss: to speculate which ones were blind; which ones had been brought back to the surface for rest and green grass; which of them would be going underground again, and which ones were played out and on the way to the knacker's yard. They climbed to sit on the top bar of the gate.

From that position they immediately spotted the limp, round shouldered girl. She was barely two yards from them, and sitting almost inside the hedge. Clearly she was trying to be private in the shelter of the thick hawthorn. She was struggling to contain her misery. She was unable though to totally blanket the involuntary sobbing within her slight body.

The boys jumped down from the gate and ran to sit either side of their friend Betty. As both boys put their arms across her shoulders she could no longer hold back the tears and the sobs. They gave her understanding time to release her unhappiness before they questioned her.

"Has the Black Cow been after you again Betty?" This was more of a quiet statement than a question from Harry. Both of the lads intuitively sensed that the nun was the problem: she always was. The nun was the prime promoter of trouble for all of them, and they knew that she had been having a go at Betty the other afternoon. Practically dragged her through the Village back to her billet by the garage, they had heard.

Gradually Betty calmed down and gradually, under their caring, concerned coaxing, the story of her past few days was brought into the open. The injustice of it made them very angry.

Harry was all fired to attack the Evans men. Without thinking about all the implications of precipitate action he was inclined to get to the garage as quickly as his legs would take him. His only plan was to take them on, separately or together.

Joe, though no less angry, was more restrained. He was more canny than Harry, and he was realistically aware that he was rather shorter, and altogether less powerful than his friend.

The poor girl was distraught at their reaction – and particularly the image that came to her of Harry tackling the two grown men on her account.

"PLEASE ...," she implored, "You can do nothing – you *must not* do anything – PLEASE."

Hunched resignedly where she sat she looked down, and in a new introversion studied her crossed arms as she continued talking in a muted voice, "If I cause any more trouble ... They *will* do for me. They have said that. They mean it – they *will* do what they say. They are going to tell Sister Alice of anything that I do wrong. And she told me that herself. And that the next time I did do anything wrong – or moaned about anything, she would put me right!"

Despairingly she added, "I'm ever so frightened. I haven't done anything! I'm just here, I don't want to be here, but I'm here and there is nothing can be done! Two days ago that lady in the uniform tried to change things, but she had to leave me at the school ... and I was taken back to the Evans just the same."

She told the shocked boys that Eric Evans was waiting for them when the vicar and Sister Alice took her back there. His dad was there too, but after a while he had gone upstairs to sit with Mrs Evans.

"They believed Eric when he told them that I had been very naughty. He said that I had been swearing a lot – and his mother was ever so upset about the swearing – and he said, I wouldn't do anything to help in the house. He said that the garage was a busy place for him and his dad, and now that his mother *could not* do anything – she had to stay in bed, and had to be looked after all the time – they had to ask me to do *little* things – like take a cup of tea up to their mother, or wash some dishes after a meal. And that is why they said, when I had been shouting and swearing the other day they just had to bolt me into my room. No, both of them had said. No – they had not hit me, they'd only told me to quieten down, and they'd only told me to behave!"

Betty desperate for the two lads to believe her pleaded, "It wasn't like that," she told them, "It was all lies. Eric was telling lies and they believed him. I don't swear … YOU know I don't swear … And I'm too scared to shout. He was telling lies … But they believed him."

She turned away from their direct and shocked gaze, before continuing in almost a whisper, "Sister gave me a good smacking there and then. She made me bend over and she tanned my bottom in front of Eric and his dad. And the vicar."

Slowly and hesitatingly she told them, "And I know Eric was looking, and he was laughing. And Sister Alice said I had to be *made* to change. And that when I did anything wrong *I had to be corrected.* She said that to Eric, and I knew straight away that *he* was going to smack me! Cos Sister had told him that he could." She hesitated before adding quietly, "and I knew that he was going to!"

She told them that the vicar had stepped in at last, and he stopped the nun smacking her. He was angry about the beating, and he was very angry when he shouted at Eric, telling him to get his dad downstairs. She heard him saying that the house was a disgraceful mess and it had to be cleaned up. He said it was a sty!

115

And he said he did not want to hear anything more … from the sister or from me.

Eric said he and his dad were too busy to keep the house any tidier than it was. And his mother couldn't do it anymore – she was too old and too ill.

Then Betty told them that she heard the nun say, "This slut from a slum family has got to do what she's told … and I'm telling *you* Mr Evans, *this girl has got to* clean the house … it's her job to repay the family that's looking after her … in any way she can!"

As the nun and the vicar left the cottage – leaving Betty fearfully alone with the Evans – she overheard him telling Sister Alice that it was not his job to sort out these things: it would be passed to the constable the next time.

The sad young girl talked quietly and the increasingly shocked and angry boys began to understand what a nightmarish time she had been through. Her factual relay of what had happened was spoken without embarrassment. She appeared unaware of the lad's presence. Other than by venting involuntary snorts of angry disbelief they did not interrupt her account.

She told them that when the nun and the vicar had left, Eric stood her by the table and told her not to move an inch. From the cottage door he had shouted outside, towards the workshop, to where his father had deserted. "Come back in dad," he called, "They've gone!"

His father returned and for a little time the two men stood and looked at the frightened girl. She stood very still by the table, averting her eyes from their attention. Eric told his father that the nun had smacked the girl's arse. Triumphantly he added, "You missed that Dad!"

He went on, talking to Betty as well as his father, "And they told me… *that she's got to be MADE to do what she's told.*"

Then Eric had sat on the chair by Betty. She made to move away, but he took hold of her arm and pulled her towards him.

116

"Make a cup of tea Dad," he instructed, without looking up and while tightly gripping, and hurting the helpless girl. As his father left the room Eric altered his position.

He remained sitting on the wooden chair that he had pulled close to the standing girl, and he was now able to hold Betty's arm with the rigid grip of his left hand, while his free hand roamed round her back: he moved it up her thighs: under her thin cotton dress: under her knickers – suddenly to take a powerful hold of the girls bottom.

This really hurt the struggling girl, but her panic masked the pain for a silent moment, until involuntarily she whimpered with fear – and with the pain. She struggled to free herself, imploring, "Please don't … Please. No! … Please …"

He ignored her pleading. "Keep quiet you bitch," he growled. "You heard what they said! Do as you're told!" And he threatened, "Or else!" He started to stroke, and lightly pat her bottom. Then the patting became a smacking, and then clumsily he started pinching her backside and began kneading inside her thighs with his full hand.

He continued with his excited and vicious mauling. "You have got to behave … OR you're going to get tanned." Breathlessly he threatened, "I can take you young lady … I can take you – across my knees – and I can learn you what's right!"

He continued – but he was shouting now as his excitement took charge of him. "We'll have your knickers off – and I will give you a redder arse than the nun bitch could ever give you!" Two of his stubby, oil impregnated fingers probed inside her body. She screamed.

His son's excited shouting, and Betty's involuntary scream startled George into a run from the small back room. He stared with fascinated astonishment – at his son – his son with the girl in his power; shouting, and doing … .

Then they were all brought back to harsh reality by a different screaming voice. It came from upstairs. George's wife was screaming from her bedroom prison: her voice never heard like this before, "AAAEERRRIC! ERIC!" Then in the powerful, dominant voice that Eric knew very well, "What the bleeding hell is going on down there?" Her voice became even more shrill, and very, very loud, "ERIC? GEORGE! … George … are YOU there? What the fuck …"

There was a thudding sound, telling them that she had fallen out of the bed. She had tried to get down to them, but had been betrayed by the muscles that had been unused for so long.

It was a bad fall from the bed and she was in pain, but she managed to croak through the agony, "Answer me you bastards! Get up here! … NOW … ANSWER ME! …… *I know the GIRL'S there* … I'm coming down …"

May Evans did not come down the stairs, but struggled where she lay, where she had fallen on the cold linoleum floor. Both men fearfully rushed to find her there. They lifted and levered her back into her bed. She had been ill a long time and was exhausted by all of this.

Eric returned to the living room alone, leaving George, his father talking soothingly, trying to tell his wife there was nothing wrong down there – just Eric tripping over a chair and swearing and cussing about it. "You know what he's like!" May did not believe him: but she was very tired.

Betty was in a hunched ball. She lay huddled on the floor, in the same place she had slumped when Eric had let her drop: releasing her, so that he could run upstairs after his father. On his return to the downstairs' room he moved to her. Speaking with quiet menace, he ordered, "Come here girl! And be very, very quiet – or I might be inclined to *make* you quiet." He pulled her weakly resisting body up and tight against his own, hissing, "This is all your fault. Now be quiet, be very quiet … remember!"

He roughly grabbed at her pubescent breasts looking intently into her eyes as he mauled them. Ignoring her sad whimpering he plastered her face and lips with his slobbering open mouth. Betty struggled ineffectively. Then mercifully she took refuge in a deep swoon: she collapsed out of his grasp and on to the floor.

Her fainting broke his compulsion. Alarmed and panicking he dragged her upright off the floor, and then he shouted as again he dropped her. "GET OUT you ugly little cow! Get out! Get up to your room! Get up there to that room of yours. And not a peep from you – I don't want my Mother upset by you again… You evil little bitch!"

There was no sign of Betty moving, and he spoke in less confidence, and a little less loudly, "Go out to the bog if you have to… And then get away to bed! Get out of my fucking sight!" He shook her as he added, "You've got to go to the school in the morning, they will be looking for you. *Fucking evacuees: fucking Catholics!*"

At last Betty reacted. She was not crying any more as she came slowly but fully to her senses. She looked fearfully at Eric, who was slumped on a chair at the table side. Keeping well clear of him, she moved painfully across the room where she found her shoes. Somehow these had been kicked into a corner. She slipped them onto her feet then she went outside to the privy in the garden.

Returning to the house she stopped at the big Belfast kitchen sink and filled a cracked mug with water, taking it with her as she moved slowly to the stairs, prudently taking the route furthest away from Eric.

She heard his final menacing threat of the day. "I hope I don't have to tell that sister fucking nun of yours, just how fucking naughty you have been tonight Miss Betty Frome!"

Betty did not tell her friends all the details of her humiliation: she felt so very guilty. However she had told them enough, and after coaxing much of the distressed girl's story out into the open, the two shocked boys agreed on one thing. Harry expressed it for them both when he told Betty, "You can't go back there again tonight Betty!" Joe agreed. He had managed to restrain Harry from rushing away to confront the Evans, father and son. "Simmer down Harry. You *can* go and kill the Evans; you can kill everybody in the village if you like. But not right now, later. You said it – she can't go back there. She can never go there again, not ever! But where *can* she go?"

Alone in her distress Betty sat silently, not listening, but hearing as the boys talked, planned and schemed. They thought of some places where she *could* hide for a while. They worked out what food they could get for her, and how to keep it secret. Harry was confident that they *could* get enough food: there was always plenty at the farm.

They considered the broken down shed by the canal, but quickly discarded it as a possible refuge. There was a huge hay barn at the farm that would be alright – but only for a night or two: inevitably she would be spotted there.

Anyway the tramp was back in residence there. The itinerant was tolerated by the Jacksons: he did casual work for the farm, at no cost other than food and use of the barn. It was said that the tramp drank his own piddle – Harry had seen the bottles. They glanced at the silent girl – she would not like the barn.

Joe was convinced that they *had* to tell *somebody,* and at last Harry agreed that they had to get the help that only grown-ups could provide. But *who* could they approach? It was desperately urgent to do *something*. They had to do something … but what?

Their planning had stalled and the three evacuees started to walk without definite purpose in the direction of Bunford Cottage: Betty had become increasingly nervous and this had prompted their move.

Eventually she broke away from them and began a fast run towards the village. "I've got to run now," she shouted, "or I'll be in worse trouble." Over her shoulder she called, "Don't follow me. Please don't follow me. Don't worry … I'll be alright!"

Joe had difficulty persuading Harry that running after Betty was not the best thing they could do at the moment. They could do nothing on their own. He listed the only possible alternatives: they *could* go to either Father Daniel, or Isabel, or Policeman Round, or Mrs Hinton.

PC Round was quickly crossed off the list. The boys had an inbred respect for the police, but their Aston childhood had taught them to be wary of them. Fear was too strong a word for the instinct they had been born with. PC Round was OK, but he was a policeman!

Isabel would *do* something, but Joe knew that it would worry her sick, and she had enough to cope with at the moment: for ages she had not heard from her old man, who was at the war somewhere.

Father Daniels would be the one, but they had not seen him that day, and there was always the danger that Sister Alice would get hold of it. They thought of that possibility for a while. Separately they shuddered at the thought, and discarded the idea of trying to contact the priest: just in case!

They came to the same conclusion: it had to be Mrs Hinton of the WVS.

Chapter 18

Mrs Hinton lived with her mother in a tiny cottage that snuggled down with its adjoining twin; down the side track that led to the rear of the Cherry Tree Pub.

The Hintons were not particularly private people, but although Mary was very actively involved in the village community, no one had ever seen her husband. That made her private, and a source for the varied, day to day speculation, in the pub and the shop.

On one day her husband was a German National, and he had been interned for the duration; on another day he was in an asylum for mad men, and today he was probably behind enemy lines in his business as a spy.

Mary had moved in to share her mother's home only a few months previously. It followed the death of her father; he would have loved the arrangement. Mother and daughter were good happy friends together and the sharing was a loving convenient arrangement, planned just for the duration: when Mary's husband would inevitably be away for long periods.

Actually Mary's husband was in the RAF. He had not yet had a leave that allowed a visit to the village. His village airing was on hold.

The two young friends ran across the Green and up the short track alongside the Cherry Tree. Harry breathlessly used the lion's head knocker: the door was quickly opened. Their faces dropped as they met Mrs Hinton's mother. Noting their dismay she immediately called into the house, "Mary – two of your clients are here to see you."

She ushered them into the small front room of her home. Mary Hinton greeted them with a smile, and with her friendly manner and by remembering their first names; she was quickly able to put them more at ease.

As they explained their mission she was putting her coat on and she was ready to leave before they had finished telling her everything they knew of Betty's plight. The boys did not have to stress the urgency: Mary Hinton had been in Bunford Cottage.

She chose to ask the smaller, younger Joe to run and ask PC Round if he could meet with her at Bunford Cottage. "Tell him that I think that it is serious enough for him to be there. He knows about my concern," she said.

She then spoke to Harry. "Do you want to come with me?" she asked, and appreciated his emphatic affirmative nod. There was no way that Harry was not going to be at any showdown with the Evans's.

It was approaching dusk when they arrived at the garage. The workshop was closed. Mrs Hinton hammered on the cottage door, and without waiting for the door to be opened from within, she opened it herself and stepped into the scullery. Without hesitation she marched on into the living room. Harry was very closely on her heels.

They walked into a scene of startling distress. Their sudden entry momentarily halted all action. In that moment the room became a horrible tableau which burned into their minds.

Both Evans men were in the room: Eric was sitting, in a space that he had swept clear on the cluttered table, while his father stood by the cooking range. Both had been watching Betty, and in their noisy commentary they had not reacted to the noise of the two visitors. Both men were guiltily stunned by their startling unexpected presence.

Young Betty Frome was kneeling on the floor, distressed and

crying. A bucket of dirty water sat on the floor beside her. In one hand she held a scrubbing brush that she had been using, ineffectively, on the filthy quarry floor tiling.

She was barefoot. She used one hand to clutch the shirt that she was wearing, trying to clutch it together; trying to cover herself. The shirt clearly belonged to one of the men, and it was the only thing to cover her. It was apparent that she wore nothing else. The girl and the once white shirt had been drenched with water, and as Mary and Harry made their entrance they saw Eric continuing to dribble water onto her head from a large enamel jug which he held over her. The features of her young body could be seen: could be visualised through the thin sodden fabric.

"Oh my God!" With this cry Mrs Hinton recovered from that awful shock of discovery. She took off her coat and draped this over the now sobbing girl, who was already being supported by Harry. He was lifting her to her feet. Mary told Betty to get all of her things. Once again she was taking her away from this nightmare place.

Eric got down from his table perch and began to bluster. His father went upstairs.

"What the hell do you think you're doing?" Eric spluttered. "Who the fuck do you think you are … breaking in like that? …The nun's in charge of that wench, not you. Now get out!" Gathering courage with his blustering, he moved towards Mary. His courage dissolved and he backed away when he found that young Harry, the big lad from Jackson Farm, was standing in his way.

"Just get your shoes Betty; that will be enough for you to take just now," said the white faced WVS officer, ignoring Eric. "We can ask the Police to collect anything that you haven't got right now."

At that exactly right moment PC Bob Round, splendidly huge in his helmeted uniform, rapped on the room's door, and without pausing he joined them. He took charge.

With the arrival of the constable Harry was glad to be released from his duties at Bunford Cottage. He took his farm responsibilities seriously and now he had very little time in which to meet up with the evening milking. Joe was sent off as well, happily running home to tell Isabel all that had happened in his day.

Bob Round remained in the cottage. He had to talk loudly above the din emanating from Mrs Evans in the upstairs room, as he cautioned the humbled men. Grimly he promised them further investigation. He went through the arrest procedures calmly and talking as quietly as the din from Mrs Evans allowed.

Finally the police constable told George that *he* would not be taken to Burton cells that evening, but that was only because of Mrs Evans's need for continual attention. "But that care *will* be sorted out, and you *will* be joining your offspring and going to Burton very soon – and to court – and I have no doubt that you will both go on to prison," he had said, not attempting to disguise his disgust for the two of them.

Eric had said nothing as the arrest was made. His life had been blank and miserable before. Now he was staring at a blank and frightening future.

Mrs Evans was still screeching as the Constable was finally able to leave with Eric his prisoner. He told George Evans that he should go up and quieten her down, but then, with his immediate job done, PC Round raised a hand and stopped the older man from leaving the room.

He allowed himself the luxury of even more freely telling both men how he felt. "I have never liked you dirty pair. But I never knew; I could not have guessed … just how dirty, how filthy you are. You are animals – no you are worse than animals. The village will be well shut of the Evans, the pair of you. Because, if you didn't guess, then I'm telling you now: you are going inside. It will be for a long time. And when you do get out – make sure that *I'm* not still here. Better still – just don't come back!"

Mary with her arm around Betty led the way back to the Church, back to the Rectory, and back to Reverend Humphries. At the

Rectory door she ignored his greeting, pushing past him into the hallway. "Is Mrs Turner in?" she asked.

Hearing that his housekeeper was indeed in the house, she demanded that she be called and asked to take the shivering girl into the kitchen and give her something to eat and drink. The astonished sweating vicar complied and Mrs Turner was quickly on the scene. Without a question she placed her hand on Betty's arm and made to gently lead her away. The girl hesitated at the doorway and turned towards Mary with an unspoken enquiry about her coat that she was still wearing. "Borrow it for a little longer Betty," Mary responded, "Borrow it, *have* it as long as you want." As the pair left the room she added, "You have been so very brave my dear girl."

Somewhat goaded by Mrs Hinton leading the way into *his* sitting room; taking charge of *his* household, the vicar regained some composure. He invited her to sit down and then demanded, "Kindly explain what you are doing Mrs Hinton."

She selected an armchair and carefully arranged herself, allowing her anger to subside. Following that chaotic, awful experience she could do with some time to think. God, she could do with a drink! She could not ask for one from this pompous prat though.

Angrily, but with a tight lipped control she then narrated all that had happened, starting with the disgraceful dumping of the young girl into an obviously dangerous situation.

"*You* and the Catholic Sister are two people who have so much to explain Reverend." She paused and allowed her anger to cool before continuing, "But now you can put something right."

She told him that, to his shame, he had the only spare accommodation in the village, and that Betty Frome was therefore and hereby billeted at the Rectory.

She told the astonished Vicar that this emergency billeting had been agreed with the local policeman, PC Round, the Allocations Committee unanimously agreeing that the Rectory was an entirely suitable temporary billet for the unfortunate girl. She herself would arrange for the girl's belongings, including her ration card, to be brought round to the house tomorrow.

The sweating Vicar made a poor attempt to argue this. He protested weakly, "But … it's impossible … for a man in my position to accommodate a young girl … in this bachelor home … different faiths, alien cultures."

Mary Hinton ignored these increasingly feeble objections and blatantly black mailed the man. "I am, as you know Vicar, a member of the Parish Council. You may not know it but I am nominated for, and will become, Chairman of the Council on Thursday of this week. In this capacity I am arranging a meeting with the Bishop, our Bishop, for the following weekend. In the interim I am preparing a secular statement of parish affairs, including our perception of this church's performance. Do you understand what I am saying Reverend?"

The battered man gave in and voiced no objection when Mary sealed the arrangement by suggesting that Mrs Turner join them. They had to settle sleeping arrangements and other such details. When she answered the Vicar's call and joined them, Mrs Turner was told all that Mrs Hinton knew about Betty's stay at Bunford Garage.

The vicar offered Mrs Hinton a drink. He was obviously in need of a drink himself so, shamelessly, and graciously Mary hypercritically accepted a large whisky and soda. She immediately felt much better. Happy with her drink; confident with the resolution of the major problem; even comfortable in the reverend's company – only concerned about Betty.

Mary suggested to the housekeeper that perhaps she could keep Betty away from school on the next day. Mrs Turner was in emphatic agreement.

Yes, there was so much to be discussed at the school. There were necessary meetings to be held with the Priest; the Sister, that dreadful nun in charge, and of course with the Police. Bob Round had arranged with her to give a statement in the morning.

Mary glanced at her watch. Contact had to be made with Betty's mother. Altogether the poor girl had had such a terrible experience; a day's rest – and, dare she suggest perhaps a day of caring – would be a wonderful and vital start to her recuperation.

Happily, Mrs Turner had already taken Betty to her heart. Without knowing *all* of the events leading up to the girl's arrival, and long before she was to hear the chronicle of evil, Betty was in her caring embrace.

It was an unpleasant night for both of the Evans men. In Burton jail Eric was kept sleepless. In succession, flint eyed police guards rattled their bunches of keys across the bars of his cell. At Bunford cottage his father spent all of the sleepless hours trying to placate his ill wife and trying not to think of what would happen next.

George's fatigue was not eased the next morning when he wandered across to the workshop. There his life was further fractured when he discovered a wide pool of oil: an envelopment of oil. It was spread across the side yard, across the rusting equipment, around the littered scrap, up to, and under the workshop door. Elsewhere the oil had gone to ground among the grass and weeds.

The tap of a fifty gallon drum of lubricating oil had been hammered open allowing the precious golden-black, irreplaceable liquid to escape. Silently, smoothly and unstoppably it had covered an immense area of the yard. Relentlessly following its own gravity-inspired route, it continued its flow under the wide steel door and through the workshop.

In normal times this would have been a disaster for the two-man business; in this time of war shortage it was a catastrophe. There was no way that the oil could be recovered. It had been further corrupted and made irrecoverable by a large monogram in its precious pooling at the entrance to the garage. There, sculpted with carefully positioned lumps of coal was a large **'B'**, and beneath it, the inscription – 'LOVE JOE'.

With no apparent anger or distress George slowly returned to the cottage. There he sat motionless at his wife's bedside. She was sinking fast. Her body was failing her. George did not tell her about the oil and the disastrous wreckage of the yard and workshop. He had already forgotten it, and she could hear nothing anyway. The very occasional clang of the bell calling for service at the petrol pump was ignored. Indeed it was not heard, by either one of the couple.

After afternoon school, in the immediate aftermath of Betty's traumatic experience, Father Daniel tackled Sister Alice. The building was deserted and the Priest's normally soft and quiet voice was unrestrained and angrily loud.

He told the bristling nun of his frustration with her intolerance, her bigotry and lack of compassion. *She* would be the school's witness at the inevitable court case. *She* regularly boasted of being in charge of the children; now she could learn to accept the responsibility that came 'with the stripes.'

He told her, "You are a naturally vindictive person; your spite towards this girl left her in terrible danger: it should haunt your conscience – though I doubt that it will – for long. This school needs a teacher; but sadly at this time the teacher is *you.*"

"You are a sadistic bully" he railed. "I cannot insist that you are sacked; although God help me, I pray that you will be. I have already suggested that you be recalled to your order. My formal request – which I will submit to the cardinal directly – will strongly recommend that you are never again placed in charge of children."

He paused, before giving the badly shaken, and by now faintly protesting woman an explicit order, "Change!" Then more loudly he demanded, "Change! For you own sake, and for God's sake change."

But he knew the nun *could not* change, and he had already discovered that no teacher was available to replace her as quickly as he wanted. Sadly he was aware that Sister Alice was going nowhere for a week or more.

Chapter 19

Brian Harding was looking for Frank, and he was looking with a purpose. On the previous Saturday he had been to the Kids' Matinee at the town cinema, and since that rare treat he had been leading his gang in re-creations of the short Western film that he had seen: the Lone Ranger.

He had watched this magic with wide open eyes and mouth, but now his limited imagination was wearing thin and the games aping the film were waning. Today's tracking down of rustlers was a replay of yesterday's non-event. Even his closest crony 'Tonto' – Jimmy Giles – no longer paid proper attention to his direction and leadership. Fatty Evans was bored and even Sam Evans, his five year old brother – normally thrilled just to be in the Company – sucked his jumper sleeve and rather wanted to be at home.

The novelty of lighting a fire behind the privy and out of sight of the houses was a past excitement. It was a small fire, more smoke than flame. It was enlivened now by some fresh sticks placed on it by Tonto who put his dirty face close to the ground and blew vigorously to encourage the dying flame. He looked up, startled by Brian screaming, "There he goes … the Varmint."

Brian had spied Frank walking in the direction of the privy. "I knew if us Posse waited on this bluff long enough we'd get him. He had to mosey through this scrubland to get to the Badlands."

Looking at his greatest admirer, "Don't just stand there Jim …Tonto … head him off before he spots us. He knows we're the Law and he'll fire his pistol and warn his no-good gang that we're

130

here." Tonto listened to more exact, exasperated, instructions from the gang leader before trotting down to the day-dreaming Frank. Little Sam tried to keep up with Tonto, but soon gave up, tired and bored. Fatty Evans with unaccustomed effort, managed to lollop a less than enthusiastic half way, before he also retired from the mission. Flopping onto the trackside grass he waited for the action to come to him, justifying his rest as an ambush.

Carrying on alone Tonto reached his unsuspecting target and challenged him loudly. "Hey Frank. Brian's got something for you." This was too nice and out of character, and he hastily corrected himself. "Frank!" he shouted, pointing towards the privy, "Lone Ranger is up there … and you've got to go up and see him … up there." … And you've gotta go right now. With uncharacteristic initiative he added, "His Dad says you've got to go!"

Frank was wary of Jimmy Giles and past experience kept him out of his path: he avoided him as he avoided Brian. "What does he want?" he asked, "I just seen his Dad. He didn't want me then, so what does he want now?"

Tonto was of like size to Brian, and his equal as a bully. He now moved up threateningly to the much smaller, younger Frank. "You'd better move it Frankie Boy. This ain't an invite … it's an order!"

Looking around him Frank could see no way past this slob of a bully. He consoled himself with the thought that he needed to go to the privy anyway. He shrugged, and as he walked past him, he muttered, "I ain't scared of you Jimmy Giles."

At the privy area Brian dramatically stepped out from his cover. "Well if it ain't the double crossing low life rustler hisself," was the rehearsed greeting from the Lone Ranger. He was prepared for the encounter, holding two short lengths of old clothes line.

"Hold him Jim … and you Fatty," he commanded. Frank was struggling now but they easily wrestled him to the ground. "Sit on him Fatty," ordered Brian who, kneeling on his face-down victim pulled his arms back and tied the ropes roughly around his wrists and ankles – unprofessionally but effectively trussing him.

Frank being rolled over was terrified to see the fire so close to his feet. He strained against his bonds. The fire was now burning fiercely. "You ain't getting out of this you thieving no good rustler," Brian spat. "We had a mind to hang ya ... but that's against the law ... like putting your brand on other cowboys' steers is against the law. So you are going to get Lone Ranger's law." Then acknowledging his chief accomplice, "And Tonto's law." Resignedly and finally adding, "And Fatty and Sam's law!"

Frank was struggling and shouting loudly for help, but his tormentor was well prepared. He quickly stifled the cries of his victim winding a dirty cloth rag over his mouth and knotting it behind his head. The Lone Ranger had thought this plot out in some detail and he now produced his last prop. It was a pea-shooter, acquired from an unfortunate and smaller classmate at his school – a metal tube with a flattened mouth piece at one end, and great fun for projecting dried peas at unarmed victims. He had practised and could spit a pea that would sting. He stood a few feet away from the trussed-up Frank and fired several peas at his face and bare legs, moving progressively closer to get a more satisfying response from his squirming victim.

He passed the shooter to Tonto, gave him some peas and inviting, "Have a go Tonto. Put some lead in him." After a few half-hearted puffed shots from Tonto, the others chose to not take a turn with the shooter. This was more serious than their usual mischief and there was not a lot of fun in it.

Jimmy moved to release Frank. "Shall we let the rustler go now Brian?" But Brian was not finished. He hated Frank with a sickness that he could feel in his stomach. Frank should not be here. He should not be in his bedroom. He should not talk with his sister, she should not even like him – and he shouldn't talk to his Dad – most of all he should not talk with his Dad. He truly hated it when his Dad spoke to Frank. Although any talk was invariably only an acknowledgement in the passing of a day, or an instruction to do or fetch something.

"No, I have got plans for our ugly little Catholic," Brian grunted. He placed one end of the tin pea-shooter into the glowing ashes of the fire. The other gang members watched in silent shocked fascination, and Frank struggled against his lashings. Brian, after finding the tin was too hot for his bare hands, looked around before tearing several dock leaves out of the ground. With these to protect his hand it was bearable for him to take the tin tube out of the fire. Without hesitation, and with no warning, he planted the blackened end onto the inside of Frank's left knee.

Frank arched his back, his muzzle failed, and his shriek panicked his tormentors. Little Sammy Evans tearfully scampered off in the direction of his mother; he was closely followed by his fat brother. They in turn were pursued by Jimmy who stuttered, "I'm off Brian," before lumbering away, his head filled with the image, the sound and the searing smell of the awful moment.

A scared Brian dropped the pea-shooter, and he too ran off, leaving Frank, still tightly trussed, crying and in pain.

"What the bloody hell are you doing Our Kid?" was Joe's reaction several minutes later when he found his younger friend in this state. "Can't leave you alone for a minute … lucky I came along ain't it?" He released Frank who fought his tears and gradually controlled his involuntary sobbing. They inspected the seared flesh. This was already blistering into a perfectly round wound, angrily red and very painful. A scar he would carry for life.

"Bastards … the bleeding bastards," Joe repeated again and again as he was told what had happened. His friend hobbled a little distance to show that he was not crippled. Joe asked him what he planned to do.

It took little time for Frank to consider the question before replying, "Nothing. What's the point in telling anybody? He *might* get a strapping from his dad – but his mom will say it's my fault – and I'll be in more trouble." He choked back his self-pity. "I'm fed up Joe. There is nobody, is there?"

"Well there is me Nipper," said Joe reassuringly, and after a thoughtful moment he qualified his question, "I meant – *what are WE going to do?* Because you are right: there's nobody you can tell. You're bloody right about not telling his mom or his dad. You *could* tell Father Daniel I suppose – but then Saint Alice would know. You don't want that! No bloody way!" He shuddered, "It would be *your* fault straight away. That's because you're a bleeding sinner. No, you certainly can't tell the Black Cow. She would have you in the flames of hell in a minute all tied up in rosaries."

In silence they shared this awful image for a short space of time before Joe continued. "Something's got to be done, and it's got to be done by us. If he gets away with this he'll do it again. But what is worse, the ugly bugger could kill you next time."

The friends sat for some time. They chewed long grass stalks as they talked. The burn wound was inspected regularly. They were impressed by its weeping, but although it was sore and the hurting was bad Frank no longer moaned. He could even feel a little proud to have this unusual mark – this badge, or medal. Finally Joe resolutely declared, "You and me Nipper! That's who is going to sort this out! We need a plan. There won't be two or three on to one next time." They plotted.

Toying idly with the pea-shooter which Brian had dropped in his panicky departure Joe, only half-jokingly, proposed, "We could shove this up his arse I suppose."

Some two hours later Frank limped back to the house, and walked into a grilling from Edna Harding. "Where have you been you little bugger? There were errands for you. I had to send Brian to the shop – and he was late and all – and they'd run out of proper fags … he came back with bloody Pasha! Now you'll miss the dairy. Don't just stand there. Get the milk jug and run! Quickly – you surly bastard." Frank took the enamelled jug with its enamelled cup top, washed it and left the house without a word. This was no chore; he liked fetching the milk from the farm dairy.

It was always bright in there: white and well lit with lots of electric lamps. The cows would be out of the parlour. You never went during milking time, but afterwards when they had cleaned up and were cheerfully pleased to see you as a customer. Often Cyril, the boss dairyman, would fill his jug cup with the warm, creamy milk, for him to drink there and then. And sometimes, not quite so often, Frank would be given a crusty, misshapen chunk of raw sugar from a jute sack in the corner of the butter room. This was special extra-ration sugar for the farm's jam making. It was a war time treat for a sweet craving boy to remember.

Today Cyril sensed that something was wrong. "Have you been crying little'un?" he asked. "What is amiss with you son? What's up?" Reacting to this kindness Frank filled up for a moment, and then explained that he had fallen off a wall, and he was alright, really, thank you.

Cyril was thoughtful as he reached for the enamel cup that Frank had taken off the jug. He filled it with the warm creamy milk, and then going to the jute sack he selected a large rough lump of sugar as an extra treat for the lad. For more than a week the dairyman was the only grown-up to comment on the blistering wound. Perhaps during that time he was the only one to see it.

It was some time later when Father Daniels spotted the branding wound, it had matured into a large, perfectly round, but still angry scab. He asked Frank how it happened. Clearly it was not an injury from a fall. He was given no other explanation; the tight-lipped priest did not quiz the clammed-up, embarrassed boy.

However he tried, Frank could not hide the roundel or camouflage it all of the time. He tried especially to delay the time when Mrs Harding would see the injury. For whatever reason, or no reason at all, he knew that when she did spot the wound it would spark her anger, her simmering anger with him: she would explode. It would be the excuse for him to get a thumping.

Her son, nervously expecting exposure and retribution, had waited for Frank to scream everything to everybody, as he himself would have done. He had not thought that Frank would keep the event to himself.

Brian could not hold the branding secret for more than a few days. He had to expect the belt from his dad, but he reasoned that he could, perhaps get away with just a shouting from his mother. He had to relieve the tension: the uncertainty. He waited for what he thought would be a good time to air his guilt; he had to catch his mother in the right mood.

The chance came just a few days after the branding and amazingly it was remarkably easy for him: a piece of cake. Actually it was several links of sausage that prompted the timing for his confession. Mrs Harding was really pleased and flattered that the butcher had held the sausages back: under the counter, off the ration and especially for her. She was quietly humming a tune as she returned home with her booty and, without trying to guess why, her son recognised that this was the moment.

Trusting his pre-emptive, self-protective instinct Brian cautiously approached the unusually happy woman, and he put his fate in her hands. "Mom. I've got to tell you something," he whined. "The other day Frank hit me, honest he really did hit me. He took me by surprise." With no reaction from her he went on, "I hit him back – like you told me to. I hit him back. I hurt him back quite a bit Mom!" He gave his mother a thoroughly edited account of his heroism.

So, on the dreaded bath day the following Saturday Mrs Harding had not been surprised to see the angry brand on Frank's leg. She was curious to see it: he was relieved that she seemed to ignore it. Following the last of the four Hardings he had been pushed into the bath by the bigger boy.

Having made his confession Brian was cockily safe now, and he boasted as he bullied Frank to the bath, "I have kept it warm for you Knobhead," then confirming, "I haven't forgotten to piddle in it for you Frankie boy!" It was a bad bath. Mrs Harding had a thin lipped grin of approval for her son, as he left to get dressed. She turned to her victim. She scrubbed, immersed, and ducked again the scared and struggling, hated evacuee.

"We have got to get your scabby miserable carcass clean you little bastard!" She intoned, with rhythmic satisfaction as she scrubbed and pummelled him. Ignoring his choking, tortured writhing she grunted her threat, "I *will* get you clean you nasty toe-rag." She landed a final thump on his upper arm, "And don't you ever, ever, ever … hit my son again!"

Frank survived. Gasping and hurting he was at last able to partly dry himself. He used the driest end of the queue sodden towel that she threw at him, and then he emptied the bath water, bucket by bucket, into the yard drain. Silently and efficiently he mopped the kitchen floor, as he usually did, but this latest nightmare of a bath triggered yet another change in eight year old Frank.

He was cleaner: he was harder, and with not a bit of childish self-pity he found himself thinking with a purpose. He did not debate with himself about the injustice of it all. It was not a question of fair or unfair. It was what happened to him: it was his life: his lot and therefore it was entirely normal.

Without conscious knowledge or reasoning, the toughened boy instinctively knew that he – Frank Bourne – had to *do* something in order to be Frank Bourne and stay Frank Bourne! He seriously believed that he could *die* in the next bath! What could he *do* to prevent that?

What could he do, to stay Frank Bourne? The answer came that night.

Frank lay quietly under his thin grey blanket. He was on the canvas camp-bed that had arrived at the cottage with him. He shared Brian's room; always uncomfortably aware of his tormentor's presence on the single bed opposite to his own.

The room was normally a safe place for him: there was no privacy within it, and the noise of any movement or fight would immediately be heard in every corner of the cottage; it was a cardinal sin to make a noise when Bill Harding was at home. You just didn't do it.

Frank could survive; he accepted, as part of his fee for being there, the gratuitous pinches and punches quietly served to him when he and Brian were alone.

The wooden planked floor was dusty; the nominal thin curtains were showing their age; there was a small rickety wash stand with a cracked marble top, and there was one small, pegged rug. That sat by Brian's bed; it was hinting of a pattern and a colour from times past. There was no lamp in the room; the ceiling pendant mourned for a bulb. It was denied one by the needs of the blackout; the useless threadbare curtain, and the demands of the officious ARP warden. The entire village would hear the door hammered and his raucous, "BLACK IT OUT! There's a war on!

Frank wondered, unhappily, but calmly, what it would be like to die. He had a good idea what it would be like to *drown*, and he immediately cancelled that line of thought. The nightmare image of his breathing being choked off by water was intolerable. Breathing was living. *Not* breathing was death. And death was escape!

He writhed in his narrow bed, then stiffened and controlled himself as Brian reacted to the movements, moaning a protest in his sleep. But could he just *stop* breathing? Could he do this? Was this a possibly painless way to escape?

Of course it wasn't! Suicide would be no escape at all: if he succeeded, *and died*, he would go hell, to the worst possible catholic hell. On the other hand of course he wasn't a *real* catholic anymore, so perhaps he would not go to that hell. But suicide was not an option, even for non-believers; non Catholics, like him and Joe.

The wide awake boy experimented. He stopped breathing. And in his first attempt to *not* breathe he found satisfaction in holding his breath for a long time! Brian, after another recent treat for him of a visit to the town cinema, had argued that Tarzan could hold his breath for half an hour! Not even Brian's cronies believed that, but at this sleepless time Frank was positively inspired.

He continued with his experiment, and joyfully he became convinced that this could be the answer! He would practise at every opportunity, day and night, from now – until the next time she tried to drown him.

She would not be able to hold him under the water long enough to drown him. Not if he could hold his breath for a long, long time. Not if he didn't panic. 'Do not struggle.' he thought. 'Do nothing but concentrate on *NOT BREATHING*.' He would be Tarzan – not as good as Tarzan; not *so* long – not even a quarter of an hour – but long enough! This was what he would *do*. Grimly, he persevered, taking another deep, lung stretching breath.

Chapter 20

Increasingly Frank found himself talking to and sharing parts of his day with the very quiet Emily Harding. Nearly eleven now, and some two years older than Frank she, like him, escaped from the house whenever she could. They often joined company, perhaps walking along the canal that ran less than a hundred yards away from the cottages, or shared an errand to the shop or the dairy. Prudently, and without conscious planning, they took care to leave and return home separately. Emily instinctively knew that she would be in trouble if her Mom found out that she was 'talking' with her hated lodger: Frank knew that he would probably die! He would certainly get a good battering.

Within days of the branding Emily was studying the wound on his leg and showing genuine concern. The pair was sitting in a secluded spot, a sheltered place which they often visited, leaning against the old stone wall of the farm's orchard: safe from nuisance and more importantly than anything else, well clear of Brian and Mrs Harding.

"Poor Frank," she murmured, "It looks very sore. Does it hurt very much?" Silently, and he thought very bravely, Frank shook his head. He liked Emily being concerned; he was flattered that the older girl had time for him; talked and walked with him. Being eleven years old was too far off for him to aspire to. He did think that he should be out of short trousers at that age; but with Mrs Harding you never knew.

He enjoyed the girl's gentle stroking of his leg. He did not know why, but it felt good and even exciting when she accidentally touched his inner thigh.

"Are you really angry," she continued, "Why don't you tell Dad about it? I know that it would be a waste of time to tell Mom; it would *not* help. Anyway she knows already – I know that – our Brian gets away with everything." She paused, "But Dad would be angry, and he would be on your side."

Frank remained silent, enjoying this sensation of feeling good; feeling just *niceness*. Looking into his eyes Emily very quietly and softly asked, "Don't you want to hurt him Frank? Get him, like he got you. Wouldn't you like to hurt him?" It was not a question needing an answer and Frank remained relaxed and silent. She persisted, "You must want to hit him – like with a brick or a big stick?"

Then, touching his face she impulsively asked, "Frank. Would you like to hit ... *me*?" He was startled, and stared at her. She went on, indignantly, "No – not like you would want to hit *HIM* – You must want to *punch* him: just bang him on his big nose, and his big mouth!" More gently she cajoled, "You're nice! Quiet like, and nice – but I'm one of the *bad* Hardings! Wouldn't you like to smack me, smack my bottom?" Still touching his face she said, "I think that you should. I would like you to!"

Frank could think of nothing to say, and before the bemused boy could even think about the proposition, or blurt any response, she continued with enthusiasm, "Phyllis Ridley told me about this game. It's called Mothers and Fathers she says – silly name – she's played it with ... ," she paused to think, "I won't tell you his name – but she says it's fun – and it makes you feel really good. It doesn't hurt – not like if your dad or your mom ever smacked you. But you could tan *my* bum instead of trying to belt our Brian. Look, I'll show you. I'll smack you first ... Just to show you!"

He found himself moving compliantly to her guidance, rolling face-down across her lap. She slipped one strap of his braces off his shoulder, and Frank himself intuitively eased the other strap clear.

Looking down at the grass below, with unseeing eyes in burning face, he was aware that his short grey trousers were being tugged down. Then more gently they were pulled down to below his knees. He felt her cool hand on his bare bottom … And then … Wow! The shock, the painless sting of the first smack.

He heard Emily murmuring, lullaby-like, as she smacked … smacked … And smacked again … His startled, uncomplaining, unresisting bottom.

"You won't tell anybody will you Frank?" she asked anxiously when he moved to sit up. When he grunted an emphatic head-shaking "No!" the relieved girl dictated, "You must spank *me* now. I have been naughty as well you know!" and she placed herself obligingly across his lap, while at the same time easing her knickers to her knees.

Frank enjoyed this part of the game less than being spanked himself. He really did not want to hurt Emily. He liked her ever so much, but she insisted that he played properly: he was instructed to spank her a bit harder.

Later, after they had looked; with honest and clinical curiosity at each of the other's private parts, and having studied the differences which were the cause of so much giggling at their schools, they tidied themselves. They reinstated trousers – hurriedly and self-consciously – and knickers – with less urgency – over the fresh pinkness of their bottoms.

Without embarrassment they talked about the experience, and they agreed that they would tell *no one* – not even Phyllis, not even Joe. They knew that they had been naughty, but it was a *nice* naughtiness – that had indeed felt good. Frank was the more mixed up of the two. He was rather confused.

"It ain't a sin," he declared, "It is not a sin. I know it isn't." An image of Sister Alice entered his head: "But I would not want to argue that with anybody." He asked for, and got, reassurance from the girl that this was a secret that they both would keep forever. Seriously and with no embarrassment he told her, "I've always liked you Emily. It's OK to live at your house – but only 'cos you're there. *You make your house feel better Emily!"* Emily leaned across, and she kissed him, a hard film star kiss on the mouth.

Later in the week they played the game again but, Emily, who was in all ways older than Frank, knew that he was not comfortable with the game. He found it very nice and he cherished the warmth that it created which he and the girl shared. He did not recognise it as the warmth of love.

He had lost track of love, for by now his mother was a shadow at the back of his consciousness, and the natural love of his infancy was in the haze of that shadow. He could not remember love. But he was too young to match Emily's excitement, and the spanking was not a natural thing for him to do. It was not *quite* right. Yet, although he was convinced that they *had* been naughty, he was able to debate with himself and argue, with equal conviction, that it was *not* a sin: he would *not* have to confess it. That was a relief!

The walks together continued. They were comfortable and happy in each other's company. Emily did not suggest the game again. It had been a very interesting and *nice*, experiment. Occasionally, self-consciously, they hugged, and now and again, rather more self-consciously at first, and thereafter more naturally they kissed. Eager kisses with eyes closed and lips tight.

More importantly they shared time: time to gossip; time to discuss village and school happenings; dreams; cinema visits that Emily had been treated to; people; friends – and enemies. They were friends, really friends. They were friends with a particular bonding secret.

They shared all secrets. Emily talked of more conventional games she shared with Phyllis and Edith. She described her day at the Protestant school, and the school teachers that she and her friends either endured or enjoyed. The pair laughed easily together.

That is until Frank, in an unguarded confidence described to her his regular and predictable bath day nightmare. Although Emily *knew* her mom, knew her moods and powerful angers, and knew – Brian excepted – that her mother hated all boys, she was shocked by the disclosure, and found it difficult to believe. She was horrified to think that her mother's unreasonable hatred for Frank might indeed have developed into such a horrible thing.

Emily had to be loyal. This was her mother! She found it hard to see how the events that Frank related could possibly have happened. How could it have remained hidden; when her dad and she herself were in the house at the same time? She tried to think of and explore different possibilities – accidents even – which could make sense of it all. Her mom had slipped! Frank had slipped! However – the water torture – had happened in every bath, on every bath day for Frank.

Then he told her of his plan: his plan for survival, and she knew that it really *had* happened. It was true: it *had to be* true: he really believed that he would be drowned at a bath time – soon.

She became totally convinced when Frank showed her how he practised his deep breathing. He demonstrated his breath-holding capability. Taking an extended breath he held it deep within his lungs, and he retained it, on, and on, and on.

He insisted that she try, but her attempts to match him at the exercise were pitifully short. No one could train, and work, and *do* that, without a compulsive need. He also confided to her that he was going to run away.

When? Very soon now. He knew the way, he was pretty sure that he knew the route home. Well he knew which way to start.

Chapter 21

The Sunday bus ground to a stop at St Theresa's Roman Catholic Church in Burton. The young evacuees from Roslington spilled from the bus obeying Sister Alice's instruction. They left the vehicle and walked to the side of the parking area, where they waited. There was no more than an occasional illicit whisper.

Suddenly the fearful voice stopped all whispering, and it halted Frank dead in his tracks.

"Where do you think you are going Bourne?" she screeched. Frank had been haring across to where another quite similar single deck bus was pulling up. Jean – *Jean his sister* – was on the rearmost seat of that bus. She had seen him and had been waving frantically to attract his attention.

"Come back here Bourne! Quickly! Immediately!" the Sister screamed in her ferocious harsh voice. The dejected Frank returned to the group, and then, at her insistent gesture he walked up to the black robed nun.

"It's my sister Jean on that bus," he told her, trying to explain his apparent mutiny. "I haven't seen her for ages." In reply she snarled, "I don't care if it is the Pope on that bus!" Adding with cold cruelty, "and your sister will be better off without the contamination of your nasty company!" She pointed at the assembled children and hissed, "Stand back in line immediately!"

At this point a young nun approached and spoke softly to the senior sister, "Good Morning Sister. Isn't it a lovely day? And isn't it wonderful that the Bourne children meet like this at the church.

I believe that you are Sister Alice, but of course you won't know who I am. I am Sister Felicity. How do you do?"

Sister Alice remained forbiddingly silent, and the young nun continued, "This is not our normal place of worship, as you know, but we are here today with the children from the Whycham and Sudbury areas who are going to be confirmed at Saint Theresa's next Saturday." She continued seamlessly in her soft quiet voice. "As you know the Bishop is here today and he has particularly asked to see the catholic evacuees who are to be confirmed. Father Brown tells me that I shall be meeting the Bishop later. I am so excited, and I do so look forward to telling him about *this* particular and happy little reunion."

She breathlessly blackmailed the angry senior sister before her. "Can I take the little Bourne boy to sit with his sister for a short time? And perhaps he can stay with our little party for the Mass? I will make sure that he is back at your bus immediately afterwards!"

She took hold of Frank's arm and led him away towards his sister: there was no argument from the inwardly raging Sister Alice.

The Bourne children met, and they were happy and comfortable companions for more than an hour. Not hugging, not kissing, not moaning or boasting: but contented siblings. Frank had little information or news to give to his sister Jean, except to tell her to keep out of the way of Sister Alice if she ever got close. They laughed together when he told her how Joe had named her the Black Cow. "Pass it on!" he told her. He did not tell her about Mrs Harding and Brian, but he did point out his friends Joe and Harry to her, and he told her about another friend who was Emily, and she was a protestant. She was about the same age as Jean was, and she lived at the same house as he did.

Jean had lots of news for him. The first shocking information was that their sister Rita had been taken away from Whycham! Jean thought that she had been taken to a convent in a place called Wales. At Whycham the sisters had been billeted in different houses but they saw each other frequently. In recent times they had not met for Rita had missed many days at the school.

She had been billeted with a woman who was known in the village as being a bit strange. The local children claimed that she was a witch. They avoided her, fearfully crossing to the opposite side of the road when Miss Bryant was walking in the village. She seemed to be very old, but wore very colourful, young though old-fashioned clothes. Most times when she walked she would have one or both of her two black cats with her. Sometimes the animals would be prowling on long leather dog leads, but in bad weather they were protected from rain and wind inside an old fashioned pram. Miss Bryant trundled this in the road itself, and Rita said it was a baby carriage.

Like the children many of the grown-up villagers also crossed the road, to move away at her approach. Her regular walk was to the village grocery shop, and there she said only the bare words necessary to get her purchases. The items she bought were predictable and they were usually ready for her visit – including her tobacco. She did not laugh, smile or talk very much at all. She did not threaten at all – other than by her eccentricity.

Rita had told Jean that it was alright staying at Rose Cottage with Miss Bryant. She *had* said that she liked the cats very much. Miss Bryant was alright and not *that* funny, although it *was unusual* to see her smoking, and enjoying *a pipe*. She sat by the fire and except for the light from the fire there was no other light in the evenings and they sat in the dark a lot.

She usually had to cook her own food – but that was alright – there was always enough to eat, and if she asked for advice Miss Bryant would show her how to cook something. Although her guardian did not talk very much, or very often she now and then bought her a cake or some biscuits, and once a fortnight Miss Bryant used both of their sweet coupons at the grocers, putting the goodies into a tin for Rita to pick from.

It seemed that Rita became rather quiet, not prone to childish excitements. It was perhaps reflecting her billet with the strange lady, but she said she was alright, and she looked alright. But if she was happy she was also lonely, for no other child than Jean would go near or speak with her.

Then surprisingly Rita did not appear at school. She had been absent for nearly a week before the school inspector, with one of the School's teachers visited Rose Cottage. They found that Rita and Miss Bryant were ill. Although managing to nurse and look after each other, they were quite poorly.

When Jean asked her teacher about Rita's disappearance she was told that her younger sister was suffering from scabies and she had to be looked after somewhere else. She was assured that she would be well again soon but she had to be kept away from all contact with anyone else. Scabies was a serious illness that was easily passed on to other people.

Frank did not tell his sister that he knew all about scabies; he had been one of the victims of the epidemic when it reached Roslington. He did not know why, but it was a shameful thing to have the disease; you were not a victim, you were a villain. You kept quiet about it, not even telling your sister.

Jean went on to tell him that her teacher said that their mother had been told. Their mom knew where she could contact Rita.

After the startling news of Rita, Frank was made much happier by Jean's account of her own life in Whycham. It made Frank feel good because his sister was really happy living over the butchers shop in the village. She lived with an Uncle Wilf and Aunty Maureen. Living at the Butchers! It was her first experience of having any importance.

She helped in the shop and worked hard, especially on Saturdays when she had the most errands to run. The big wooden chopping block was her biggest chore. She explained to Frank, with enthusiasm, how she had to scrub it, using very hot water, a sharp wire scrubber and a hard bristle brush. Then she had to dry it thoroughly with mutton cloth. She took a lot of pride in the task which was rewarded every time the block dried to the required whiteness.

Uncle Wilf always said "Well done." It was really nice to hear him say that. *And* she was paid pocket money: she showed Frank a three penny bit that she had, as well as a penny for the plate in church.

"Aren't we lucky Frank? Being here, in good places ... with nice people ... not in horrible Birmingham, where our mom has to stay while Hitler's bombing it all the time."

Frank thought about it, but he made no reply. The butcher's shop sounded great. Birmingham sounded great as well.

In Birmingham their mother had not had time to find out more about Rita. She meant to go to the church on Sunday to ask how she was getting on, but there was no chance at all that she could get to see her in the convent in Wales.

Apart from the pressures of work, travel was practically impossible. The travel she *could* do was compulsory – to and from work – and now she had been told that she had to get out of Lichfield Road. Pretoria Court was another of the rows of slum housing scheduled to be demolished within a matter of days. The bombs had done much of the slum clearing work in the area already, but now it was too difficult, dangerous even for the Council to maintain the electric, gas and water services. The slums were going to disappear completely.

It was to be a new exciting, no-regrets start for Gladys: she had been allocated a council house in Tyburn – with a closet inside the house – and a bath, in a bathroom!

She was going to change jobs as well. Albrights had so far survived the heavy bombs, but several incendiary droppings had caused a lot of disruption and insecurity. Everyone believed it to be only a question of time before they would get the 'big one' that would destroy the factory, and probably them as well. They were worse off in the crowded together factories of Aston and Nechells than the big new, more spaced out factories which were along the Chester Road at Castle Bromwich.

A lot of aeroplanes and aeroplane parts were being made in these 'star' factories, and everybody knew that the wages for skilled, experienced workers were highest when you made aeroplanes, or bits for aeroplanes.

From her new house in Tyburn she could easily get to Castle Bromwich. Her planning now was to go 'sick' on the coming Thursday. That was the day when she would get the keys to her new house. On that same day she was going to get herself a new job.

Tyburn was near Erdington as well, and Gladys's new man friend lived in Erdington. Alfred was several years older than Gladys. He was a toolmaker at Albrights, but intending to transfer his skills to the aircraft work himself. Together they thought the move to Tyburn was splendid news.

Tonight after work they were meeting again for a drink. Gladys knew it was inevitable that she would be going to bed with him. Soon, – perhaps tonight.

Chapter 22

Frank had been living in Roslington, staying with the Hardings for years, forever it seemed: in youth three years is forever.

During all of those months life had *not* been unmitigated misery. There were many all-right days like weekends and holidays, and the fireman's fete.

Being at war was no big event. It was something in the background for Frank and his contemporaries: something now and again highlighted by the wireless report of 'Al Varlydell', following the daily raids into Germany, intoning the number 'of our bombers who are missing': keeping the score, which now suggested that we were winning.

There were good days at school. Sister Alice – the Black Cow – was an ever present and looming danger, but with care she could be avoided, or deflected into the path of an easier victim. Instinctively they obeyed simple rules of self-protection. Never look into her eyes; if you looked at her it was a challenge that invited the ruler across the knuckles. Never stray into her territory because if, carelessly, you got too close, you were asking for a pinch, a slap or a thump in the back: painful awards for getting within reach. Most important and easiest rule was to stay silent, and be small!

Father Daniel was OK. It was good to do well at reading, writing and sums because Father Daniel liked you to do well. It was nice when he told you that he was pleased with your efforts.

At home Mr Harding was OK: a neutral presence who accepted

Frank for what he was. If he thought about it at all he reasoned that the boy was not there because he wanted to be, it was not his fault, and neither threatened the other in any way. Bill Harding was fair. He made sure that Frank was given free time, and Frank valued his freedom. He was always on top of his routine chores and even Mrs Harding had little to chastise him for in that respect.

Sister Alice at school; Mrs Harding and her son at home, they were the only ever present threats of danger: impending doom, pain and unhappiness. Frank countered by keeping as insignificant and as out of reach as he could. He was good at being small.

Brian had been quiet for some time after the branding. Frightened when he recalled the game that went out of control, but nothing had surfaced. He had told his mother, and he had got away with it. Emboldened he reverted to his normal noisy, bullying presence, and unfortunately Frank could not always avoid or ignore him. Joe declared that something *had* to be done about Brian, and Harry Clayton, the third member of the *Slummy Brummy* gang, agreed.

Harry was thirteen years old. He was of sturdy build, quietly spoken with a deliberate, no nonsense nature. Mrs Jackson had made a good selection at the billeting allocation. Harry worked long, hard and – if he thought about it at all – happily at Jackson farm.

The three Birmingham mates did not think of their association as a gang, but having poached the *Slummy Brummy* title, from the jibes of village boys, they now openly and proudly identified with it. The village youths, having lost the slogan, and with it the high ground, and after suffering a few subsequent skirmishes, prudently rationed the insults and jibes.

Unsurprisingly Harry accepted the younger, smaller Joe as natural leader of the group. The three boys did not think they were led by anyone, but Joe was the ideas man. Invariably he was at the front of their adventures; he did not clown for laughs, but he was instinctively funny, and without fail he was fun. They were happy to follow where Joe led, if only to see what happened next.

He was in a more serious mood today. Frank was sporting fresh arm bruises. With Brian on his mind Joe asked Harry if he had any ideas. Harry always thought before he spoke: this was a question requiring thought, so without waiting for an answer from the deliberating youth, Joe turned his attention, and the same question to Frank.

"Have you thought any more about getting your own back with our best friend – our Brian?" He asked Frank. "I still think that you should get him up here. We could all sit on him. I can't see why you don't like that idea?"

"No!" his friend answered, "It would be blooming obvious that it was me who arranged it; you don't know Mrs Harding! It would end up hurting me much more than it would hurt Brian."

The three boys squatted with their backs comfortably braced against the old, unused and disintegrating wooden shed, at the edge of the canal. They often convened here, usually without making any prior arrangement: they gravitated to the place. They guessed that it belonged to the canal owners, but that did not stop them making it their own. It sat behind the wild hedge that grew parallel to the canal towpath. Sheltered from view and curiosity it provided a rare privacy for the boys.

Today they were recovering from attempts to make and smoke 'cigarettes'. It had been a choking failure. They had shredded dried cabbage leaf with their finger nails, and had patiently wrapped a scrap of newspaper around the leaf bits. But the leaf was more old than dried, and the paper tube had merely introduced hot paper-smoke into their throats. It was Harry who released them from further experimentation by declaring, "Got no more matches!" Thankfully they put cigarette smoking on hold, and without this unsatisfactory distraction they were able to talk.

They talked about the school. About the Colliery Band that continued to bring colourful exciting noise into the school's timetable. That was usually on the last Friday afternoon of each month; they looked forward to it.

They speculated on the evident friction between the Black Cow and the freshly arrived, younger nun, Sister Cecilia. Harry reckoned the smiling new teacher looked good enough to kiss and hug. Joe agreed, he did not really know what 'one' was, but it did not sound out of place when he said, "I could give her one!"

They agreed that Sister Cecilia had made a considerable difference to the school day. Her smile and laughter were cherished, and her supervision on the clapped out single deck bus each Sunday transformed that event. With noisily missed gears and stuttering clouds of smoke, the old bus transported them to Mass at St Theresa in Burton.

The young nun led the singing, not on the way there to solemn Mass of course, only on the way back to Roslington. The young sinners loved it. They loved her. She let them sit wherever they wished: boys and girls together.

Joe and Frank joshed Harry about his girlfriend. On the Sunday bus Harry invariably sat with Betty. They didn't talk about *that* day: it had never happened. Betty was happy at the Rectory and it showed in her happy face. She worked hard for Mrs Turner, they shared a loving respect. Reverend Humphries tried to be aloof, but he encouraged her to learn; introduced her to books; coached her with homework, and together they listened to music, which they later discussed.

The Reverend Humphries had changed. Most Sundays he would walk with Betty to the catholic church bus, and on the bus's return he would be waiting to escort her on the short walk *home*: to the Rectory. Both of them, having completed their Sunday morning churchly duties, looking forward to Mrs Turner's Sunday dinner. This was a major change in his Sunday routine. Mrs Turner had suggested that a *proper* roast dinner would be *nice* for Betty, and it would be grand if they could all sit down at the same table at least once a week.

After the awful events of the Evans and Bunford Cottage and

after just a single night's stay at the Rectory, Betty had been whisked away to the main convent in Birmingham. She had been subjected to a frightening, almost sinister series of psychiatric and medical examinations: with all the nature of a court case – with herself standing guilty and on trial – before a succession of suspicious nuns and priests.   Within a week however she was rescued from her ordeal by the unexpected arrival at the convent of Father Daniel. He reassured her that she had done nothing wrong, explaining that certain questions had to be asked in certain situations. She accepted that, understanding that Bunford Cottage had been such a certain situation. He asked her if she wanted to go home to her family in Birmingham, promising to take her there himself, and to take her there immediately, if she *wanted* to go *home*.

The Priest was relieved that she chose to return to Roslington. He was relieved at her choice because earlier that day he had visited Betty's home in Birmingham. He had met her mother before, but was still astonished to find that she had very little concern for her daughter and her welfare. He was rather surprised however when Betty asked if she *could* return to Roslington. Many of the youngsters in his charge had a distorted perception of *HOME*. They chose to remember it as a happy, almost holy, nest of joyful love: a place waiting breathlessly for their return. He marvelled again at the resilience of children and wondered why he had been surprised by Betty's decision.

The priest then found it necessary to camouflage his delight, for Betty asked him shyly if she could stay at the Rectory: she would like to stay with Mrs Turner, if she could be allowed to. This had been the preferred resolution of the 'problem' of Betty. During the time that she was being challenged at the Birmingham convent her future during the continuing evacuation had been discussed and decided in the village. Debated mainly at the vicarage where Father Daniel had a newly found friend in the vicar. Mrs Turner, Mary Hinton, Father Daniel, *and* the vicar at several discussions had arrived at the same conclusion.

The very best place for Betty to be billeted and rehabilitated was the Rectory. They all wanted her to be placed there but, after the trauma she had suffered there could be no further coercion – this had to be *her* decision. So when Father Daniel returned, with the pale and nervous girl sitting with him in the front of the car, they were met by the welcoming committee in the Rectory driveway, all of them equally relieved and openly delighted with her decision.

In the vicar's mind it would be a stay for life, for the Reverend Henry Humphries was a changed man. Acknowledging the danger into which he had carelessly exposed the girl – and his own previous arrogance and prejudice – he was now a newly tolerant man, an involved and more caring shepherd for the parish. In which his change was beginning to be noticed, and starting to earn a growing respect.

Initially, because of his guilt, he had cared particularly whether Betty stayed, or went back to what he perceived to be a grey life: a life clearly without care and without the immediate affection, care and attention that could be hers at the Rectory. Then selfishly he recognised the changes in *his* life that Betty's arrival would bring about. Her presence would give a purpose to the place, a purpose to replace his previous and boring preference for uncomplicated routine.   Happily the reasoning and judgement of all of the parties working for Betty was proved right. With her quiet uncomplaining acceptance of all things coming her way, her naturally happy character now blossomed. She showed an open appreciation of the friendliness and support she was showered with. Her appetite for knowledge, for music and for books grew. She enthusiastically enjoyed the regular good food, and under the undemanding mutual respect and love she had for Mrs Turner, Betty Frome flourished.

She occasionally met up with the *Slummy Brummys,* usually arriving with Harry, but she was not at this meeting today when Joe, Harry and Frank covered the wide range of their recent experience. When they did meet with Betty they never talked of her traumatic first billet and its resolution. Now and again though she would tell them of her present life, her changed life at the Rectory. She would talk enthusiastically, passing on trivial but interesting Parish gossip, or talk of the latest book or music that she had enjoyed. The boys delighted in her happiness, a happiness so much deserved after that awful time.

Chapter 23

Betty's rehabilitation had been helped considerably when Eric Evans pleaded guilty at his trial. Because of this plea she was not required to recount all that had happened to her at Bunford Cottage. The evidence that was very clearly presented by the Police Constable, Bob Round, and the unequivocal statements and presence of WVS Officer Mary Hinton, were sufficient to send him to prison for four years of Hard Labour. Eric was a destroyed man.

Bob Round was to confide later, that in his opinion, Eric *had wanted* to be sent to prison and *away* from the village. He *had* to leave the village – the garage, the petrol pump, his mechanic's status, and livelihood. The place where his mother and father had lived worked and reared him – where his parents and he had lived – and where his parents had died, was a place he could never return to.

May Evans never recovered from her fall. She died within two days of the 'event' which occasioned her fall. She died just one day after learning that her husband and her son were the Monsters she suspected them of being.

An ambulance had been called to take her to the town hospital, but she chose to die as she was being carried down the stairs, strapped onto an upright kitchen chair. She *called it a day*, and silently May Evans died. The two ambulance men carefully easing her chair; carrying her, step by step downstairs, had not noticed that she had escaped. They saw that only when they placed her chaired lifeless body in the centre of that godless room. By her death she was spared sight of that room, and death released her from her awful imagination.

The ambulance, booked to take May to the Burton General Hospital took her instead directly to the morgue there.

The same ambulance returned to Bunford Garage a couple of days later to collect May's husband George.

George and May – husband and wife – had never been apart: his wife's departure to the hospital was, in his memory, their only separation. He sat alone, with the knowledge of her death and the heavy guilt of his treachery, for all of that day. He sat unmoving before an ash filled cheerless grate, needing neither food nor drink, feeling immeasurably unhappy and empty to his core.

It was late in the night when George had crossed from the cottage to his workshop. On his passage he had found himself with time to recall the enormous pride that had been his when he and his young May had first acquired the place. He again tasted that pride. It had been salted with apprehension at the start of the bold venture.

He recalled the continuing pride, and the satisfactions, the joys, the fears, and even tears, that May and he had lived through while building a worthwhile business from nothing.

Tears were streaming unchecked down his grey stubbled cheeks as he allowed free passage to the memories of the years. Eric did not enter the old man's memories.

George found himself rolling an empty fifty gallon oil drum through the workshop. Strange that the drum was empty – he could not recall emptying it – and how untidy the shop had got he thought – he would have to get the place cleaned up a bit.

Carefully he positioned the drum directly under the sheave: the sheave high above him in the roof. He had clear recollection of fitting that sheave pulley, on that roof truss, so many years ago. It had earned its keep he thought: it had been invaluable for lifting engines out of cars, and work pieces off the floor.

He relived some of the work that he had done over the years with it. It was threaded now with an oil soaked rope. Methodically he secured the rope's end to its cleat.

When he kicked the drum away the oily, age stiffened rope was nearly, but not quite, elastic enough to allow George's feet to anchor on the floor. It allowed his boots to lightly touch safety – and with that touch it teased him into instinctively reacting to the possibility of survival. Arguably the sheave with the rope had failed in their last task, but they had not failed, they had not let him down.

PC Round found him the next morning: George's boots barely above the workshop floor. The dirty floor; still glistening with recently flooded oil, was scuffed by his feet's instinctive, involuntary attempts to gain a life-saving purchase.

Chapter 24

Betty was not at that day's get together when the three boys discussed at some length the edifying philosophic conversation enjoyed by Frank earlier in the day. He had been on his way to meet his friends at the usual canal rendezvous when the Road Sweeper, sitting on the lane's grassy verge had cheerfully greeted him.

The newly met and friendly workman was finishing his lunch. They exchanged names: George and Frank. George invited Frank, the thin gloomy faced boy, to sit down and rest for a while.

"Everybody is in such a hurry today," he said. Joining him on the grass Frank was delighted and astonished to be offered an unforgettable custard pie! Always hungry, and always conscious of his hunger, he immediately recognised that this was more than mere food. It was not merely to be devoured. It was an experience: a wonderful taste and a sacrifice made by this new friend. His gift to the man in return was the transparent enjoyment with which he very slowly ate and relished the pie.

It was a warm autumn day and there was no hurry in either of them. They comfortably exchanged confidences. George had been in the First World War. When asked if he was going into this one he told the boy that that was not possible – except he was already in the war – they all were. Frank told him that his dad had been in the Great War as well. He did not think he was going to be in this one because he had been gassed and shot; he further related that he had not seen him for a long time, both thought about this for a while, and thereafter they spoke no more about *that* war. But his new friend went on to explain things about *this* war: things that Frank did not know and had not thought about.

Now, later in the same day, when he told his friends of the conversation, they agreed that they did not think much at all about the ongoing war. They thought much more about food and the Black Cow of course: those were ever present considerations; the war was happening somewhere else. It was more than keeping a score – about the number of our planes that were missing daily after bombing raids on Germany.

The road workman put real people into the numbers: he put flesh and blood pilots and crews into the planes, he also put bombs in the planes, and he placed flesh and blood people underneath the bombs. People quite like *them*; he said – evacuees, road sweepers, teachers – were under the bombs, in Germany the same as in London and Birmingham.

The boys afterwards did have a truer understanding of the radio news that they heard most days. Usually in a grown-up midday silence they heard the news reports, but now they found more meaning, and some colour in the reports.

The veteran road labourer's philosophy did not in any way change the way the boys felt about the German enemy. Perhaps they *were* evacuees, teachers and other things, but they were not like them. They were Germans and foreigners, and the boys hated them. They hated them because they had been taught to hate them. Everyone knew that you would be a traitor if you started to feel sorry for the Germans. They were the enemy. They had started it! It was the German's fault that all of them had been evacuated – Hitler had forced them from home – when they only wanted to be at Home.

Joe and Harry put this interesting roads worker on file. They would look out for Frank's friend: the custard pie friend.

Meanwhile there was brave, yet fearful talk about Sister Alice, this in turn sparking yet more discussion about the new Sister

Cecilia. Gossip that the children had picked out of the air was that Sister Alice was being recalled to her convent, and she was in the process of handing over to Sister Cecilia. The Black Cow had been sacked they heard.

The idea of the school without Sister Alice was intoxicating, and prayers were widely offered asking that this come to pass. *Please Mother Mary!* It was the best possible thing that you could look forward to: equally as good as winning the war would be. Certainly the rumour was strengthened by the changed and more subdued nature of the tyrannical nun. However, the experienced, suspicious scholars continued to keep clear of danger. They stayed out of finger pinching and ruler smacking range.

Fearfully Frank approached the school office; he could not think what he had done wrong. What had he done to bring him to this unusual summons? Father Daniels and Sister Cecilia were in the small room waiting for him. The young Sister regarded him with a compassion that the nervous boy did not see. The priest touched his shoulder and invited him to sit down at the desk in the chair facing his own. The nun stood behind Frank, and again Frank did not notice that her eyes were brimming with tears.

Father Daniel was leaning over the desk. He looked very serious; speaking in a low, very concerned voice he explained the summons.

"I'm so sorry Frank … but I have to tell you that your brother David … is dead!"

He had not softened up the boy to receive this awful news. In his experience there was no preparation one could make for tragedy. It was an event that could not be concealed. It should not be delayed, and it could not be parcelled to be anything other than what it was. He hoped that when he had given the tragic news, he would be able to provide some comfort and help for the lad. But first the news had to be given, and there was little point in telling the boy that he would *not* be seeing his brother again, or employ any other euphemism to disguise the fact that David Bourne was dead.

He gave credit to Frank's intelligence, talking to him as he would talk to an adult, while at the same time watching him closely and measuring his reactions. He told him factually all that he knew himself. HMS Hood had been in a glorious battle in the North Atlantic. A single shell from a huge German ship had found the weakest point of the Hood and entering the ammunition storage it had destroyed the British ship. And with it – bar three – it had taken the entire crew.

"It was instantaneous Frank! It happened in a split second," and optimistically lying the Priest added, "Your David would not have suffered at all."

Frank was the centre of attention: he was more aware of this importance, than he knew what it was all about. Why? He had very little recollection of Dave, who throughout Frank's life had lived with their Gran. He had seen him but rarely. They had shared very little conversation; had played no games together; had shared no adventures. He had always been proud to say that his brother was in the Navy – had *been* in the Navy he corrected himself – but although he was sad, he was not as distressed as was expected of him. "Did they win?" he asked the Priest, who reacted in surprise, to ask him what he meant.

"Did they win?" Frank repeated, "Did the Germans win?"
Father Daniels told him that the Germans had not won: the mighty Bismarck had in turn been sunk by the Royal Navy. As he told him this he realised to what extent war propaganda had fashioned this boy; there was little doubt that all of the boys in his charge had this cultivated hatred within them. It was a hatred that transcended grief.

Information of the revenge eventually brought down on the German ship was the best comfort that he could offer Frank. It was better than rhetoric, better than tears, and more comforting than prayers.

Thinking that something was expected of him Frank spoke. "Dave lived with Gran." And Father Daniels understood immediately why Frank was less upset and less grief stricken than one could anticipate: he came from a splintered family, a unit normal to the slums of any city. The splintering devolved responsibilities and diluted love itself. Emotions were mostly physical: centering on food; anger; lust; warmth, and money. Grief was a luxury.

Father Daniels suggested that Frank could go home for the rest of the day if he wanted to. He would arrange for someone to go with him.

"Can Joe come?" Frank asked with initiative, "Can Joe Dunn come with me?" And so the two boys spent the remainder of a warm day, not in a claustrophobic school room, but sitting at their favourite hideaway place, talking and throwing stones into the canal: the cut. They talked about big ships, huge guns, death, drowning, Sister Alice and the nice new nun.

Chapter 25

Gladys suffered the unique pain of a mother losing a son. She could not avoid the grief any more than she could afford to take time off from her new job. Dave had lived with her mother for almost as many years as he had lived with her, and his father. She had few of a mother's normal remembrances: delight of childish achievements and shared joys. She had always been too busy, too poor, to see any of her children's development in detail. But, he had been at her breast and he had taken part of her with him – to his Gran's, to sea, to battle and to his death. She grieved, and she thought of Bill; wondering how her husband was taking the news. Cynically and unkindly she pictured him at his pub that evening downing free commiseration pints.

Without the natural partner for her grief, she was comforted in her grieving by Alf's presence in her house. A widower for some years, Alf Smith had been happy to move out of the gloomy bed-sitting room he had in a Victorian house in Erdington. He was fed up with sharing the bathroom and the kitchen with the increasing numbers of Irishmen now in main occupation of the house.

The single men had been recruited in their own country, enticed to work for the good money to be made in Birmingham. Money to be drunk, gambled or sent home. Cleanliness of bathrooms and kitchens is notoriously low on *any* single man's list of priorities, and Alf was more than ready to move from the factious tinder-box of lodging.

He was a great companion and comfort for Gladys,

166

contributing more than his share of the rent and housekeeping, and now providing the solace of a needed shoulder for her; easing her mother's grief.

Alf knew about her children, who they were and where they were. His own two boys were grown men now, living and working in different parts of the country; he doubted that she would meet them; he had not seen them himself since their mother had died.

His particular skills and experience pretty much guaranteed that he could get a job in the same factory that Gladys had moved to. When the job was settled he promised her that one day, when it was suitable for both of them, he would arrange for a car owning friend of his to drive them into the country. They would visit the kids.

"Let's be sure of each other first," Gladys suggested. It was so unreal for her to have someone who thought like that: someone senior, someone who cared about her.

They had no regular need or inclination in the evenings to go to the pub now. They stayed at home; they cleaned and adjusted the house; lit a fire; listened to the radio. They enjoyed each other. As they talked and planned for after the War, with the growing optimism that each day's news started to give them, Gladys found that with her new security came a new emotion: an unexpected happiness. Not the ecstasy or bliss of youngsters coupling, but more the enjoyment of their shared bodies, and equally the satisfying discovery of their like minds. Two people needing and attaining the same fulfilment. And she found now that she had time – outside of the day's survival priorities: time in which to think.

She thought a lot about Dave, and found that it was easier to remember him as a baby than as a young man. She found herself thinking, wondering, and worrying about Rita, and increasingly she thought of Charlie, and Jean, and Frank.

Ellie she worried about, but could discount this as a major worry, for Ellie was her own woman following the path of her choice; and young Joan – well she was more her Gran's daughter than her own.

She was no longer able to think of the children's separate and divergent lives as being solely brought about by their father's disappearance, or entirely the fault of the war. Gladys began to recognise just how limited had been her acceptance of responsibility for the children. She acknowledged her selfishness, and she accepted the guilt that the recognition brought.

Alf talked through all of these worries with her. At his initiative a new writing pad, envelopes and stamps were bought, and on successive evenings, time was set aside, for Gladys to ease her conscience: time to re-establish herself – as a mother. One by one she wrote letters to her children, Alf at her side totally committed to her cause.

The first letter was sent to the Convent in Wales. It was a difficult letter to write, for in her entire life Gladys had never had cause to write a letter. It was addressed to Miss R. Bourne – strange to think of little Rita as Miss R. Bourne! She imagined her daughter ill, and alone in a friendless dark building in a strange country. Writing this letter was difficult for the unpractised writer. It was a strange process, and ambitiously trying to express emotion as much as fact made the letter more difficult still.

Alf helped her with all of the letters, but particularly with this first letter to her youngest daughter. With his help the message that she sent to her daughter was unstilted: it was uncharacteristically cheerful, full of optimism and love. She told Rita of the new home and described the room that was waiting for her and Jean to share, when it was safe for them to return to Birmingham. With Alf's help she painted a picture of a new city, far removed from the back to back slums of Aston, and with the letter Alf enclosed a stamped envelope with the new Bourne address on it, a pristine sheet folded inside inviting a reply.

The letter to Jean was easier: it passed on the same news, hopes and plans. Once again there was a stamped and addressed envelope hopefully enclosed: the address showing where their planned and changed future would be based.

She wrote to Charlie: a letter full of concern and exhortations to be careful. For the first time in the series of letters she spoke of Dave, and their loss of him. She sensed that Charlie was as close to the tragedy as she was. He had looked up to his elder brother; had admired, envied and loved him to the point of copying him. He had joined the Navy to be like him.

After a great deal of deliberation Gladys wrote, *'Things can be so different now Charlie. In this new house* (before the letter was posted she let Alf change that to *home*) *there is a room for you to share with little Frank when he is back at home and when you come on leave. PLEASE come home when you have a leave! I want to show you off to our new neighbours.'* And she told him of her new friend Alf. It was a long evening that she and Alf spent writing the letters: it was exhausting.

It was very satisfying, but the strangeness of expressing – for the first time in her life – so much to her young ones was a draining experience. It was uncomfortable to think of her children as 'Loved Ones' and frightening to hope that it was not too late for her to be – or become a Loved One too.

When she had finished the letter to Charlie, she needed very little persuasion from Alf to go with him to the Holly Lane Working Mens Club for a pint. They both deserved a drink. They enjoyed the quiet night as they walked, and together agreed that it seemed to be getting quieter with each night that passed. It could be a lull; only a lull, but raids were less frequent, and life was getting better.

She told Alf that she would write to little Frank later in the week, but she told him Frank was OK, and very safe where he was in the country. She had no cause to be concerned about him, and he would be the first one they would visit when they were able to buy some petrol coupons: for Alf's friend, who owned the motor car.

Later in that week Gladys found the writing pad and settled

herself at the kitchen table. Without Alf, to cheerfully bully and guide her she was at a loss how to start, what to say to her son. Then she noticed that it had started to rain. She had washing pegged out. The letter to Frank would have to written later. It was never written.

In the Convent of The Sacred Heart, remote in the northern Welsh Hills, Rita had fully recovered. She was well, and a favourite with the nuns, who had nursed and still looked after her. They had cured her of the scabies she had brought with her; all of the scabs had gone now, and no disfiguring pock marks were left, that anyone could see.

The small convent was of the Augustinian Nursing Order, and at thirty two years the average age of nuns there contrasted surprisingly with the more usual fifty years and more in the solely religious convents. It was a bright, light, and cheerful place, and when she was well enough to appreciate this caring friendliness Rita wondered if she herself could not perhaps become one of these angels.

Amazingly Rita received two letters within two days. "We know that you are a very nice young lady," Sister Imogene told her, as she smiled and passed on the second of the letters, "But to be as popular as this … Well, it's famous, so it is!"

Rita's first letter was from her mother. She could not hear her mother's voice in the letter nor could she visualise her mother's face, although she tried very hard to refresh the faded image that she had of her. The letter was happy; perhaps that explained the difficulty in relating it to her mother. She could not recall her mom being happy, and certainly not 'show off' happy.

Rita opened the pencil box – the box that Miss Bryant had given her on her first day at the Whycham School. She selected, and unnecessarily sharpened a pencil to occupy her time of thinking; then she gazed at the sheet of paper which sat, very white, on the table in front of her.

She looked out of the window at the Welsh Hills; heard, sighted and then waved to a familiar nun as she passed. She listened as the cows were called in for milking at the nearby farm, visualising the bumpy activity in the farmyard. It was nearly time for tea, and although still replete from her lunch time soup Rita never missed the thin bread and jam, with perhaps a slice of cake which was Tea at the convent. There was no contest: she gave up on the letter to her mother for a while.

The letter from Miss Bryant arrived on the following day. When she opened this, in wonder of the *who* and the *why*, Rita gave a little shriek of delight, and she continued to laugh out loud as she read the letter, while looking again and again at the two black cats facing each other in silhouette on either side of the letterhead. They were exquisite black ink drawings of Trik and Trak. Rita knew that it was Trak who sat serenely on the left, and it was definitely Trik arching his back on the right.

Miss Bryant had known that she did not need to tell her which cat was which. Rita could see and hear Miss Bryant as she read the letter of many surprises.

*'My dear Rita, I am so sorry that you became ill while I was supposed to be looking after you. During my visit to your School yesterday I was so pleased to learn that you are now entirely well. I hope that you do not object if I tell you that I, and Trik and Trak, miss you very much. I know that I am a FUNNY old Thing, and I know that – face to face – I would probably never **tell** you what I am now able to **write** to you. If it upsets you – then please will you screw up this piece of paper – and drop it into the cess pit – or throw it at the wimple of the nun whom you like the least!*

The thing is my dear Girl – you have made a big difference to my life, my every day. It may not show – my Goodness! I do hope that it does not show – what a useless miserable existence I have been paddling through in these past years. Now young Rita Bourne has brought a purpose, a meaning into our days. I like the fact that I am concerned about you. I am distraught that you should have contracted that decease while under my care. I do not know how I could have prevented you getting it – but I do feel that I have failed you. Although in my defence I must tell you that the Health Inspector has been here, and he says that it was NOT Rose Cottage which caused or raised the problem – other cases local to here had been diagnosed BEFORE you and I caught it. But Golly!! I blush to tell you that his visit did make me realise just how grubby Rose Cottage has become. I have shaken my feathers now and the place is getting a Spring Clean. I am enjoying it! It will be sparkling for your return.

I am praying that you WILL come back here. But the School tells me that you may not. Oh Dear! I cannot bribe you with the joys and fun of younger company but there are so many things in my head now – in a head that has not held any plans for years! Drawing and painting to be done, stories to be written, walking to be walked, and talking – so much talking to be shared. And all sorts of other pursuits which are there to be shared, and which when shared, are such a lot of Fun.

*Things – like sharing – are joys which I have almost forgotten. I am hoping to hear from you – a letter from Miss Bourne would be very, very nice! And it would be very, very, **very** nice if it tells me that you will share Rose Cottage with a silly old woman – who cares for you – in a more than selfish way.*

Your sincere good friend, Beatrice Bryant (Miss)'
'PS I will stop smoking the horrid pipe – if you insist!'

After this were drawn imprints of Trik and Trak's paws prowling off the paper.

Rita replied to this letter immediately. She had already told the friendly Sister Imogene about her life in Birmingham and had described her life in Whycham, with her friend Miss Bryant. The young nun, seeing the writing pad placed on the table, and, for what she saw as a special letter, gave Rita loan of her treasured fountain pen.

Rita wrote to thank Miss Bryant for her letter. She told her of the Sister's special fountain pen that she was using. In very little detail she told of the convent, and, in altogether more detail she described her new friends and the food. She told her that she had had a nice letter from her mom, and she ended by saying that Miss Bryant really did not have to stop smoking, and her friend Sister Imogene was going to find out *when* she could return to Rose Cottage.

Miss Bryant, Rita, Trik and Trak were reunited within the fortnight. In the sparkling, freshly distempered front room of the cottage, in the white light of a well-tuned oil lamp, Rita finally wrote to her Mom. She told her that everything was well: she was healthy, and very happy – and she was back at home. She promised to do a painting for her soon – probably of the cats. Miss Bryant was sitting by the cheerful fire; the cats curled at her feet. She was reading, under the more than adequate light. Contentedly Beatrice smoked her pipe.

Jean replied to the letter from her mother more quickly than her sister had done. Like Frank she had been told at school about her brother's death at sea. The news had upset her terribly. In the night awful images came to wake her, shocking her bolt upright in a panic, soaked with sweat. Time and again the nightmares woke her, and with her they woke Aunt Maureen, who lay with her in the double bed. At this special time Uncle Wilf had surrendered his place and was spending his nights sleeping in Jean's narrow bed. They all slept fitfully. The letter from her mother had made Jean weepy. She again remembered the dashing young man, and remembering the last time that they met. Dave had let her touch his blue collar – for luck. She wrote to tell her mother that she had been ever so surprised and really pleased to hear from her. She hoped that she was still well, and she thought that the Council house sounded really good.

Reading on her saddened mother then learned that Rita could have the bedroom all to herself. Jean was very happy in Whycham and she was hoping that she could stay there with her Aunt and Uncle. Her life was much, much better in the village than in any place in Birmingham. She had not spoken about this to Auntie and Uncle – Mr and Mrs Statham – but she was sure that they would want her to stay. She told her mother how much she loved the business. It was exciting and she was doing ever so well – she was trimming ribs and things now, and making sausages. She was still doing the errands and the block of course – but now Uncle Wilf had promised that he was going to teach her how to be a real butcher. She was going to be famous he said, the first lady butcher in the county!

Charlie answered his mom's letter on the Saturday following its arrival. Saturday afternoon was a Make and Mend – precious free time – however the Navy dictated that all Boy Seamen would write home regularly, and the divisional petty officer would check on the envelopes sent out. Writing was marginally preferable to the embroidery, which he would otherwise be doing – although he would still have to do that later in the day. He had to complete the red wool cross stitching around the letters of his name which he had stencilled on to some new kit. Pyjamas – fancy bloody striped pyjamas. No one could laugh at him though – they all had them – and they all had the associated chore of sewing their names on to them. He had to get it done before the next day's Kit Muster. And he had to match the new kit with his other stuff: the clothes had to be formed into the precisely regulated tight rolls required for kit-bag stowage, and as specified by the Admiralty. More importantly it was as required by the division's petty officer.

"Thanks for your letter Mom," Charlie wrote, "I will be on leave soon I think and will be coming to see you at the house. It sounds good. I was hoping to get leave when our Dave got it. They sort of promised me that – but it did not happen! Hoping you are keeping well." The letter ending with a flourishing, "Yours —- Charlie!"

Chapter 26

At their impromptu get-togethers by the canal: unplanned, unscheduled, but surprisingly regular casual meetings, the three mates shared and debated the latest news. In this particular discussion Harry was the main item. They were always interested to talk about Harry's grown-up work on the Jackson farm. Harry, a naturally quiet youth, was not tall for his thirteen years, but his increasing stockiness reflected his daily work regime at Jackson Farm.

An early start to every day: roused out by one or other of the Jacksons at half past five, fumbling into his clothes dropped on the floor of his room the previous evening to be ready for use; hurriedly drinking a steaming mug of sweetened tea waiting for him in the kitchen. Then outside, in whatever weather the day presented, for a piddle against the barn wall, before opening the big iron gate and marshalling the cows waiting there for him across the yard and into the brightly lit milking parlour. There, the big lumbering animals instinctively following the well-trod routine they knew and enjoyed, being teat washed and connected in turn to the proud new milking machine.

After the milking returning to the farm house, and quick cold water wash in the kitchen sink, with Mrs Jackson grumbling at him, and everyone else in range. As she grumbled she efficiently presented a hot breakfast to the three men at the long, scrubbed kitchen table. Not saying a great deal they were too occupied in taking on the great fuel for another day's labour: bacon, perhaps sausage, egg, potato cakes, and lots of homemade bread and, from the huge brown pot on the table, heavily sweetened tea.

Harry had become a key member of the farm team. He grew into the demands made on him by the farm – demands by Mr and Mrs Jackson, the animals, the crops, and the changing demands of the changing seasons.

Every day Harry enjoyed meeting with Ed who arrived at the Farm in time for breakfast. He was the regular day worker, a simple man in his mid-twenties who worked willingly enough when directed, but who was not blessed with a great deal of initiative. Ed and Harry shared all the routine and varying chores; Harry naturally taking the lead role. He still had to attend school and make appearances at the village hall but more often now he skipped school altogether. He preferred to work and share a long day with Mr Jackson and Ed. The highlight of this could be harnessing the two Suffolk Punches, Isaac and Ben. Towering horses that, with Ed to help him, he could now harness, singly or as a pair; getting them hitched up to the work load of the day: the plough set, harrow, seed drill, haywain, muck spreader or heavy cart.

After the morning milking and following breakfast, Harry cleaned up for the walking trot to the village hall school. Although he attended school less and less often now, when he *did* go he was very often late. During the early days of the school, when Harry first became involved with the morning milking at the farm, he had regularly incurred the wrath of Sister Alice with his frequent late arrival at her catechism class. On many days he had been obliged to passively endure her 'correction'. She was able to draw from her voluminous black uniform, and with the speed of a gunslinger, her favourite 'corrector'. This was a twelve inch long wooden ruler, the edge of which gave excruciating pain when applied to the knuckles or bare knees. It was part of the Sister's fearful presence, as was the children's knowledge of her special pinching technique. The slapping and pummelling were more *acceptably* normal.

Harry had merited top place in today's news discussion as the boys recalled a particular, noteworthy run in with Sister Alice in the earlier days of the school. Once again he had been late arriving at the Sister's catechism class, and he had fully expected the belting from the Black Cow which followed. This belting got out of hand however. His silent acceptance of the punishment appeared to trigger an exceptional outburst from the nun. Possibly aggravated by the boy's stoicism, the usual abuse of venom and bile, the spat words, the pinches and blows, had become uncontrolled. The punishment had developed into a startling frenzy of hatred, and it had been witnessed by the entire school who were gathered for catechism. They gasped when Harry's face became the target for the nun's wrath. When he had instinctively raised his hands to protect his face, and then, in trying to avoid the worst of the blows which followed, he had moved away from the Sister, she had followed him.

The punches and flailing blows became frantic. This was not a normal 'correction'. He had to protect himself, he had to get away! Grabbing the foot long wooden ruler from her hand as she scythed it towards his face Harry had stepped back, and dramatically he had snapped it into two pieces. These he had calmly passed to his open mouthed, spluttering, but otherwise speechless attacker. He then turned, and without hindrance from the Sister, Harry had walked out of the room.

Father Daniel, alerted by the unusual ruckus, had been making his way to the hall classroom when he met the boy hurrying towards the main door: the way out. Without a word the priest took his arm and had led him in to his small office.

"Let's have a chat Harry," he had said conversationally, pointing at a chair on the opposite side of his desk for the youth to occupy. "I think that this noisy rumpus indicates that you have been late yet again my son. Were you indeed late for your favourite morning lesson today?"

Sister Alice arriving at that moment, flung open the door, which narrowly missed Father Daniel as he stood between it and

Harry. Harry had stood up, but he rejoined his seat when the Father motioned for him to sit down again. The nun had angrily thrust the broken pieces of wood towards the priest. Father Daniel, as he accepted the useless ruler parts had spoken quietly, but quickly, to avoid the inevitable outburst. "Sister Alice! Harry and I were talking, and I'm sure we were talking about the matter that is on *your* mind!"

He had paused and inclined his head towards the hall. For a short time he had appeared to be concentrating on the hubbub arising from the classes still assembled there. Then he had continued in his soft brogue. "We will sort this out Sister, but perhaps you would like to rejoin your pupils now – before we have a full scale riot on our hands."

This had been said jokingly but the manner of his speech was unusually authoritative: it was not to be questioned. He had thrown the useless ruler into his waste paper basket and the furious nun had stalked out of the office.

Harry had been awarded three straps across his open palm, and had been advised to leave the farm a little earlier, or run a little faster, "But *please* do try to get to school on time."

Father Daniel eased the smarting a little when he had punned with a wry smile, "Don't … please don't break the *Rule* again!" Harry returned his smile, they understood each other. He was not attacked by the Black Nun ever again and neither was he again strapped by the priest.

Although often late, and frequently absent altogether, Harry had earned the Blind Eye.

Sister Alice wrote a letter to the Bishop complaining about the Priest's behaviour and attitude towards discipline. The letter was never posted; neither at the time was the quid pro quo letter from the Father, asking for a replacement nun.

At their regular get-togethers, usually at the canal side shed, Frank and Joe could talk almost as knowledgably as Harry about the changing demands of the seasons on the farm, particularly those where they could have a peripheral role, such as potato picking.

Their task during spud picking was to follow the main harvester pulled by the heroic Suffolk horses Ben and Isaac. As they followed they picked up the potatoes that escaped the machine. Most importantly they were paid for their aching backs at the end of the day.

Frank had developed enough nous to minimise the amount in his pocket after payment for any work. He knew that Mrs Harding would be waiting to plunder. He stashed any retained coins under the stones and gravel by the roadside gate. If nuts and raisins or other coupon-free treat became available at the shop the coins would save him a strapping he thought with a grin. More seriously he vaguely thought of the pennies as an escape fund. He did not have coupons to let him buy sweets with his booty: Mrs Harding had the ration books and somehow only Brian and Emily seemed to get a share of sweets, although Emily would often secretly allow him a little share of hers.

At harvest time the boys would be busy with stucking, which was pulling together four or five sheaves of barley or wheat into one spot, and stacking them vertically against each other to dry out. Early on they had learned to leave the stucking at the verges of the field for the beginners. For them to learn as they had, that as you harvested closer to the field's edge more and more thistle weeds blended into the sheaves. These were inescapable; they painfully cut and scratched the bare legs and the arms that necessarily embraced them. Again though there was the promise of some payment to salve their lacerations at the end of the day's work.

Only the largest, strongest boys could hope for work and payment at haymaking, but all of them could chase rats escaping from the old ricks, as they were rebuilt with the new hay, and almost all of them would have the excitement of riding on top of the haywain. They watched the sheep dipping, collected the lambs' tails when they were bitten off and spat out: the tramp was a star at this. For all that they knew where they came from, and how, they could still enjoy lambs' tail pie at this time of the year.

The very best work experience they ever had been plum picking. Father Daniel had arranged this for the boys, and there was no lack of volunteers when they discovered that it involved a trip in an open flat-bed lorry to an orchard some miles away – *and* they could earn some money doing it. It promised to be a great fun adventure, and because of this Frank knew that Mrs Harding would squash the idea: she would stop him going.

Employing the guile he had necessarily acquired he waited until Bill Harding was at home, before asking if he could go. Bill thought it was a good idea. "You bring some home!" he said, giving his blessing. Mrs Harding was not at all pleased but she had not vetoed the permission given by her husband. She consoled herself for being 'soft' by declaring, "It will be good to have a couple of days off: a couple of days without the miserable little bleeder."

It *was* an adventure. The happy rowdy boys sang all the way to the farm. Sitting and bouncing on the dusty deck of the open air and ancient lorry, they cheerily greeted everyone they passed, and they lustily worked through their limited repertoire of songs, singing again and again the favourites: 'Lili Marlene' and 'There'll be blue birds over the white cliffs of Dover'. They ignored any melancholy in the lyrics: the tunes were the thing. In a break for breath Joe contributed an ode that Isabel had shared with him, he chanted: *'I'm Pop Eye the Sailor Man, I live in a caravan, there's a hole in the middle, through which I can piddle. I'm Pop Eye the Sailor Man!'* It was catchy, easily mastered and just a bit naughty. Irresistible. They all joined in – several times.

Arriving at the fruit farm they found that their billet for the three days of work was a huge and exciting barn well stacked with hay and straw. They had been told to bring a blanket and a towel and that was the extent of their kit. Soap was supplied at a large stone trough supplying cold water via a long handled upright pump. You had to prime this by first pouring a bucket of water into the pump top, and then you had to yank the long iron handle, up and down, like a maniac – until you won! Then you heard a throaty gurgle – the promise of water rising from the depths – and then experienced the thrill as fresh water from the well below splashed and sploshed into the stone trough. Among the score of lads there was not a great desire for water to wash in, but there was strong competition to get on the end of the handle. It was FUN. Then trays of food appeared, greeted by cheering applause: healthy sized pieces of cheese and crusty chunks of fresh bread *and* butter, and apples and plums. It was manna to the ever hungry urchins. They drank the milk and ate everything to be eaten; they sang and pranced and wrestled until a grown-up appeared and asked for their attention. When he had gathered them around him in the yard and could see that they were listening, he introduced himself.

"Call me Jim," he said, then flattered them and their maturity by asking, "Do any of you smoke?" Hearing their chorused 'NO' – none of them *did* smoke – he said he was ever so pleased to hear that, "Cos smoking means matches, and matches means fires. Fires mean burning barns – and burning barns burn hay and straw – and it burns anything else in the barns!" He ended dramatically, "It burns kids to death!" He had made his point forcefully and he had let them know that he was very happy this was not going to happen here. Just two boxes of matches were willingly surrendered when he suggested it.

At Jim's courteous invitation they followed him into the barn where he showed them how to stuff with straw the long hessian sacks that sat in a pile by the door. He told them that *all* soldiers had to make their own mattresses like this, and he offered a piece of chocolate for the best one made. They had to be filled just right, not too little, not too much, and all without lumps. He was pleased, and a little surprised that they gave him their full attention; they cheerfully did as he asked. He inspected every palliasse made; removing straw from some; stuffing more filler into others; pounding some into better shape, and shaking others down.

The boys were disappointed but resigned when finally he told them that the competition was too keen: the mattresses were all very good; it was impossible to decide which the best one was. The boys sighed, eyeing their own hopeful entries, and wondering why the man could not see just how subtly *best the shape of their palliasse was*. Then from the haversack he carried, he produced chocolate bars which, when each bar was broken into two equal pieces, provided enough to supply all of them. They were *all* happy winners!

The farmer suggested then that it was time for them to get settled down, they would need their sleep to be ready for the busy day tomorrow. They cheerfully found the latrines; a few even had a perfunctory wash under the cold water pump. They all found their gear, and with this, and a towel and blanket, they converted each freshly made palliasse into a bed: their bed in the barn bedroom for the next two nights. When Jim left them in an almost silent barn, some were already asleep; others shared a last whispered confidence. Jim was impressed by his first encounter with evacuees. They had been impressed by Jim.

For most of them the next day lived up to the expectations inspired by that warm and fun welcoming day. After a breakfast of porridge with Golden Syrup, bread, jam and tea, the older, tallest and strongest boys were taken to the orchards for the actual plum picking. Frank was one of a dozen boys left in the yard to sort the plums. A tractor appeared, and the plums – sitting on the tractor's trailer in large round woven baskets – were upon them.

The task for the boys was to sort the fruit by size and appearance into one of four boxes, the fourth of these being the reject box for damaged, bruised or not quite perfect fruit. These were destined for jam, they were told. They sat in a circle, each on an empty box, and each with a basket and four trays for the sorted fruit.

They started the work, slowly at first, because rather a lot of the finest and juiciest fruit had to be sampled, before the rest of the job could be taken seriously. They also discovered that a plum is a wonderful missile. Arguably at any one time during that first morning there were more plums in the air than in any one basket. However they worked well and kept up with the frequent tractor loads.

It was a full, colourful and rewarding time for the evacuees. For Frank it was a million miles from Birmingham, the war, the nun and Mrs Harding.

Chapter 27

At the canal side meetings, almost as a regular item on their unwritten agenda Joe would tell Harry and Frank, and any other casually attending friend, of the latest happenings at his billet: the cottage he shared with the dotty Isabel and baby James. Joe was happily lodged there. Haphazardly looked after, casually cared for, and loved. All of the school envied Joe.

Today he was concerned: Isabel had not heard from her Old Man for weeks, and she was reacting badly to the lack of news. She thought he was in Africa. He was not a great writer but Isabel had the dreadful sense that something had happened to him. The irregular letters and postcards had stopped completely, and with each day that passed without news Isabel became more introspect, losing her natural frothiness, and as she laundered and ironed more infrequently, and brushed her hair less often she became a little less pretty.

Joe spent more time with the baby James. He knew that she appreciated this, it was something she didn't have to think or mither about, and he was happy that he was able to do something that might help her through this bad time.

His friends shared Joe's concern, although to a lesser degree. Isabel always gave them a friendly welcome when they called at the cottage for Joe, or when they met her in the village. She was more of a friend than a grown-up, having an innocent openness and interests that were tuned to their age. She *was* a bit dotty, but there was no hint of a threat in her. Joe had told his Mates of a pillow fight that had left Izzy and him helpless with laughter; rolling on the floor before the gurgling appreciative baby James. One warm summer's day she had found him asleep on the small garden's patch of grass, and with a bucket of water had drenched him, before seeking to escape shrieking with laughter. This time of worry now contrasted blackly with the normal times of so much laughter at the cottage.

However the main talk among the friends today was last Saturday's Pig Sticking in the village. The brutal event had left indelible impressions on the evacuees. In the past couple of years they had all seen killing, but it had always been the casual easy paced dispatch of a chicken. A twist and pull of the neck, or more occasionally, and more dramatically, an axe taking the chicken's head off. Now they witnessed a killing procedure – a ceremony.

Most villagers reared chickens, and several still had pig sties in their rear gardens, sties which had survived from busier simpler days past. Some were now housing the chickens, but most of them had a new role: storing logs, coal or come-in-handy paraphernalia. Today the war, and more particularly the rationing regime, had brought pigs back into some of the sties. And today a pig belonging to a miner was to be killed.

The sense of illegality about the killing enhanced the excitement, for bypassing the food rationing system by acquiring food without coupons, was unlawful – equally as illegal as killing some living thing. There was therefore a pervading sense of secrecy and urgency about the entire affair. But of course the whole village knew. Knew it was going to be done, and where, and by whom. Those villagers, who had been regularly contributing scraps for the swill feeds knew that they would get some part of the harvest.

And the pig knew! Unceasing screams filled the air from an early stage in the proceedings, and impossibly the screaming level steadily increased. Many found this too difficult to tolerate, and the bystanders thinned out. Several men were in attendance and more, including the *Slummy Brummys,* had gained vantage points on the path at the rear of the cottages, and on neighbouring garden pathways. Although startled – initially *terrified* – by the first screams that they heard, the three Brummy lads had to keep face, and they retained their places among the onlookers, deliberately trying to maintain an insouciance that they did not feel, exposed as they were to the incessant piercing din.

Jim Hatton was the man in charge. He was an underground miner by occupation – and a respected killer of pigs. He had considerable experience and justified a reputation earned in several villages in the area. A man among men, to whom men spoke deferentially – when invited to.

It was not an everyday happening, and the easy competence of Jim was impressive. He displayed experience in the methodical way he went about the preparation for the killing. Firstly he had lots of straw and old hay spread over the work area that was in and outside the wash house, the place of execution. The outbuilding belonged to the pig owner. Earlier that morning, at Jim Hatton's instruction, he had filled the large boiler with water, and had lit a coal fire under it, which he still tended. The boiler was built into a corner of the wash house – and in good time the water was ready, raised to bubbling point by the well maintained coal fire.

A block and tackle with a hook on its bottom sheave was suspended from a heavy timber rafter high up in the wash house roof, its pulling rope leading to a substantial cleat in the side wall. An old redundant door laid across two trestles outside the wash house completed the scene.

With the scene set two village men tugged the terrified pig off balance and onto it's back; a short rope was rapidly tied from one of the animal's front legs and then held and drawn tightly across its chest. The two men struggled with the restraining rope, and called for more weight to be applied. There was no shortage of men and the animal was quickly bundled and dragged into the wash house.

It was manhandled into position under the waiting, dangling hook. The Master deftly trussed the pig's rear feet together and hooked the tackle-hook under this binding.

At his signal the waiting men hoisted the savagely screaming beast head-down into the air. Another man, scrupulously avoiding contact with the writhing pig, placed a galvanised bucket on the floor, and nervously held it in place directly under the wide mouthed screaming head.

Jim, with one mercifully clean and swift movement, slashed with his broad bladed knife. Blood spurted. It cascaded down – down through the shrieking, gurgling, choking, and slit-open throat – and for a never ending minute, the pig maintained its grotesque, blood saturated scream. The fearsome noise draining away with the blood into the galvanised bucket.

The three wide eyed and silent boys stayed throughout the screaming. Rooted in horror they saw the pig slit open, and they watched with fascination as Mr Hattan carefully removed the bladder, noting that he pinched the bladder's top until he could tie it off with a cut length of twine he had ready to hand. With the bladder safely gone, the rest of the entrails followed, in swooshing quick time, and the vacated pig was soon lifted and placed on the trestle table for the remainder of the post-mortem.

The youths did not wait to see all of the organised mayhem that followed. With unspoken agreement they left ahead of the scalding; the bristle scraping; the axing of spine and pelvis; the sawing off of feet; the head splitting; the washing and squeezing clean of the yards of intestines.

They knew that every bit of the pig would be used, including that foul bucket of blood. They had lived here long enough to know where the black pudding, the brawn, faggots and sausages came from. These they all loved and hungered for – for a good part of every day. They were not very hungry on that Saturday afternoon. Well, not particularly hungry.

Several days later and they were hungry again of course. Sharing two acquired apples their conversations meandered. Harry had the day free, Joe was as free as he usually was, and Frank did not think that his time away today would cause trouble. Mrs Harding and the others were at Granny's house.

Frank talked little of his time at the Harding's. He did not have to tell his friends. Clearly he was apprehensive about his impending return there today, and they knew he was anticipating his next greeting from Mrs Harding.

The knowledge led them into more discussion of Brian. They had been studying and poking at the scar on Frank's leg now that the scab had fallen off. More truthfully it had been picked off – with the satisfaction that only a good scab picking could give. It was healing into a nice, angry white scar. It was a roundel brand for life, and a spur for them to do something.

"I reckon Brian needs a good hiding." Joe volunteered, not for the first time. "We've been talking about this for long enough: we keep talking about it. Let's give him a good hiding; one pasting would be enough! He don't fight you know … he only *hurts* people when he knows he can't get hurt himself. But a hiding would show him what it's like to be on the other end. He wouldn't need two lessons! "

Big Harry thoughtfully made a contribution, "He could have as many of his mates with him as he likes. But we have got to get him on his own – away from grown-ups I mean – they'd interfere … and that would be worse than us not doing anything." They planned and they schemed, and the longer time they spent on their desultory plotting the more it changed: from wishful thinking into something more tangible: something about to happen.

Joe, Harry and Frank, were again at their favourite lounging place. They squatted comfortably with their backs to the dilapidated wooden shed at the edge of the canal-side garden. It was an isolated yet entertaining spot, now and again enlivened by the rich life of the canal: a passing barge was an entertainment never to tire of.

On the towpath in the distance they would spot the advance member of an approaching barge, usually a son or daughter of the barge family, arriving at a trot – hurrying to get the canal water level correct in the lock – and the entry gate open, ready for the huge craft to come into it. Sometimes, if they were following another barge going in the same direction, it would be necessary for them to close the far gate, open the sluices with the cranked spanner looped on their wrist; let water into the lock, and then, when the level was equalised on both sides of the lock gate, open the near lock-gate to give uninterrupted access for the arriving load.

When their help was agreed to, the evacuees liked to help, pushing and pulling to close and open the lock gates. They enjoyed watching the approaching barge – with the sturdy experienced horse comfortably leaning into the tow-rope, easily mastering the boats weight. They were always impressed when, without prompting, the horse would unerringly slow as the craft neared the lock gates, giving leeway slack to the tow, allowing the bargee the spare loose rope that he needed so that he could flick and weave it into the correct running positions to negotiate the lock passage; clearing all of the obstacles of the lock, and – if they were going in the down-canal direction – the low bridge squatting immediately after the lock.

In down-canal direction the tow could not be cast off until the boat was free of the lock: it had to be pulled out by the horse that, led by its experience, would have moved beyond the bridge, and would wait patiently in this new position. The long extended tow rope was now taken from the horse, to run over the bridge's stone parapet, and back to the barge imprisoned in the lock. The lads had noted and marvelled at the long smooth grooves which had been worn in the stone coping of the bridge, worn by thousands of ropes in the tows of many years.

When the gates were opened, the horse, receiving a short, low whistle, would lean into his harness and drag the heavy vessel out of its lock-bound inertia. When there was enough momentum built up to propel the barge up to and under the bridge, the tow rope would be cast off from the barge's towing spar, and just as swiftly and slickly re-connected as the boat emerged from under the bridge. It was a complicated but seamless operation that the lads never tired of watching, always noting and appreciating the techniques and effortless skills of crew and horse.

The canal, or cut, often froze over in winter. Rarely was the ice thick enough to warrant using the Ice Breaker, but when it *was* used it was a thrill to see it in action. A very heavy barge had been converted for the task. Sturdy decking was fitted over the hold replacing the usual tarpaulins. A heavy timber handrail, fitted to a height of about four feet, ran for the forty foot length of the breaker-boat. It was mounted between bow and rear cuddy, bisecting the decking fore and aft. When working to clear the canal of ice, the Breaker was towed by an exceptionally large horse, and manned with half a dozen men standing on either side of the centre line handrail. They worked with a rhythm; one line swaying back from the rail as their opposite numbers leaned against it: slow short movements to get it started and then longer and longer heaves on each side as they got the barge rolling, breaking the ice, allowing the horse to pull them through the ice debris, clearing the canal for normal traffic.

One time the Gang was invited to join in and have a go, and their enthusiastic efforts did make an appreciable difference – but only down to the next lock.

The cargo barges were always very smart, clean and colourful. This regardless of the cargo it carried: whether the cargo under the spread tarpaulins was coal, ore, china clay, or finished china.

Inevitably they were highly decorated, with brightly coloured paintings of flowers and castles covering the sides of the living cabin at the stern of the boat. Stacks of kindling on the small cabin roof, shared the space with pots of herbs and flowers. Invariably the flue of the heating and cooking stove would be belching coal smoke; often competing with mouth-watering hints of frying bacon, or the irresistible smells of baking. The mother in her wrap-round uniform apron, standing just inside the open door of the cabin, would be tending the stove as she cooked for the brood. With kids of varying sizes the floating family comprised three, four, five, six perhaps seven or even eight bodies – working, sleeping, and living, in the ponderous, impossibly cramped, noisy, colourful, and usually cheerful barge.

The gang had got to know a lot of the barges and their families. They exchanged greetings and banter with the 'nice' ones; asking what the load was, even offering to take some, 'Just to lighten the load!' Asking where they had come from – and they always asked where they were going to – always listening for the destination Birmingham, and often hearing it.

Chapter 28

Frank sitting alone, lounging at the lock – and wandering in his usual introspection – had his reverie broken by the appearance of a young lad trotting briskly down the tow path. This presaged the arrival of his family's barge.

With little more than a friendly grunt Frank offered to help. The offer was accepted with a similar economy of words, and the pair worked together to raise the water in the lock. With this achieved and when the dock water was level with the rapidly approaching barge, they leaned their backs and combined weight against the heavy oak gate.

Frank learned that the barge was heading for Birmingham. He was thrilled; wanting to know more, and when the bargee walked with the horse down to the next lock, Frank and his questions walked with them.

His accent gave him away and the man commented, "I can see that you are from Brum. How long have you been here? When are you going back?" Frank could not answer that question, because he just did not know *when*, or even *if* he was ever going back. He was fascinated that this barge was going to his home town, and perhaps even going close to his mom.

He questioned his friendly companion, wanting to know how far, and how long the journey was. He did not get answers immediately for they were coming up to the next lock and there was work to do. But when the barge had passed smoothly through this second lock Frank was invited to jump on board, and have a cup of tea. He knew that the next lock was quite a long way ahead, but the thought that this boat was going on the right way and heading closer to Birmingham made it a simple choice. He clambered on board with alacrity, and decided to wait until they arrived at the next stop before he would start to think about the long walk back to the Harding's. Now he could only think about this adventure, and of going home – his real home.

Easing Frank's concern about the walk Dan the bargee had in fact moored up. He followed Frank onto the barge, announcing their presence by calling out cheerfully, "There's another one for tea Jenny!" then looking and grinning at Frank, he asked him his name and then shouted to his wife, "but Frank's only tiny: he won't eat much."

His wife Jenny was just as friendly as Dan. It was no surprise to her that someone had been invited for tea. Cheerfully she said hallo to Frank and welcomed him down the three-step stairs into the cabin.

The youngster was overwhelmed by their home. It was so *nice*: cosy, warm, and welcoming. Jenny was very proud of her home and she was delighted to see his open mouthed reaction to it all. The cast iron stove was burning brightly. In the glow coming from its open door, the cabin's ornaments, carvings and pictures came alive.

There were flower decorated mirrors in carved frames, the flowers naively bold, richly coloured and enhanced with teardrop distortions within the glass; lovely fragile plates, held on the cabin walls with ribbons threaded through the tiny holes cast in the edges of the china plates, and lots of brass and copper pans and jugs – gleaming and alive in the moving light. It is Aladdin's cave thought Frank.

The best was yet to come for Dan announced, "We're stopping here for tea!" He washed his hands in an enamel bowl that was waiting for him on a small table by the stove. With a gesture he invited Frank to do the same before passing a small towel to him.

"We're waiting for Donald. You met him at the last lock, he's been foraging for wood and he will be with us in a minute. He doesn't miss his tea very often!"

The couple laughed, and as they laughed they all felt the barge react as Donald stepped on board, to appear at the open hatched door. He was a year or more older than Frank, to whom he nodded a friendly acknowledgement, while he told his dad that he had got quite a bit of good dry wood. It was on the canal bank, and he would cut it up after tea. Frank was shown the bench seat he was to sit on, and they had tea.

The evacuee had never sat down to a family tea, and he was astonished by this almost ceremonial occasion. Food was an ever present consideration; something vital to Frank. It was always in his thinking. It was very satisfying when you got it, and very sad when you had *had* it. It was something to be eaten – in as large a quantity as possible, and devoured as quickly as possible to pre-empt any challenge to ownership. Bread thinly spread with lard, dripping or jam was a treat, and especially so if accompanied by tea, perhaps with sugar, and likely contained in a cracked mug.

In contrast, in this hard working industrial vessel, the tea was incongruously poured into delicate china cups; the cups balanced on *matching, and unchipped* china saucers, while a replenishing teapot of the same pattern waited in the middle of the table. The table was fixed at the side of the cabin; it was draped with a rose embroidered table cloth that Frank could see was smothered in wonderful things. Thin bread – already buttered; boiled eggs sitting in fragile china egg-cups; a jar of blackberry jam; a smaller jar of honey and an impressive two tier silver cake stand, beautifully presenting a small selection of cakes and scones.

Noting, and enjoying, Frank's open mouthed astonishment Jenny put him at ease. "There's an egg for you as well young Frank," she said, passing to him an egg sitting in a tiny cup, and then placing bread and butter on a small plate and also passing this to him.

Frank had never had an egg! He *had* had the *top* of an egg once – but that was way back in Birmingham. Brian was the only one to have any egg top now. War had made eggs scarce, even in the country – but this family had them at tea time! Dad had one; Mom had one; there was one for Donald – and he had one! He watched, and followed as others ate, showing him by example how to cope.

Seeing his slight nervousness Dan asked him, "Shall I take the top off that egg for you Frank?" – And he did this without waiting for a reply.

The tea was a memorable meal for Frank. It ended when he was invited to select a cake from the tier. The largest delight on offer was a rock cake. He looked questioning at Jenny who smiled and nodded for him to take it. It was no surprise to her or Dan that he took the rock cake. They shared a smile.

Donald jumped up and left the barge, as though he had that sort of tea *every* day. He started to work on the wood that he had collected, sawing, splitting and chopping it into logs and kindling: into the perfectly uniform sizes that would be stacked on the cabin's roof.

Dan left the cabin and sat on the stern transom, where, after he had filled his pipe with rich smelling tobacco, and had this burning as he wanted, he talked with Frank. "I reckon when your tea has gone down, you should get off here," he told him, "As it is it's a long enough walk back to Roslington from here. The next lock's more than a mile on," he chuckled, "Don will have to get us through that one on his own."

Frank was astonished to learn that the barge would be in Birmingham in just two days time. He had not seen a map, and even if he had seen one he would have had difficulty in reading it, or understanding the distances implied by it. The availability of maps, and other possible aids to enemy parachutists, was subject to more of War's frustrating restrictions. All of the counties' sign posts had been removed; even the cast iron mile posts along the canal had been taken away for scrap.

Dan jokingly told Frank that you could not get lost on the cut. You went where the boat pointed. The only decision he had to take was to turn his barge left at Fradley, by the Swan Pub. And there they had to branch on to the Coventry canal. This would take them to Fazeley where they would join with the Birmingham Navigation.

Frank swallowed with excitement and he got Dan to repeat the details for him: Fradley Junction; Swan Pub; Fazeley; Birmingham Navigation. Birmingham was in touching distance.

Dan was surprised by Frank's keen interest and appetite for information. "You're not thinking of a long walk are you son?" he asked. The boy shook his head – but that was exactly what he *was* thinking.

Dan immediately saw through this innocent rejection of such an idea: the lad *was* planning to run away. He could understand the motivation for this, and admired the boy's spirit, but he hastened to dampen down the idea, and told him, "Birmingham's a big place Frank – it can be a dangerous place and it's too easy to get lost in it. Which part are you thinking of?" He explained, "The canals go everywhere in Brum: they reckon Brum's got more canals than Venice, and that's famous for being *all* canals, it's built on canals."

Frank knew of Aston, Saltley and Nechells and Dan knew them all. "Do you know Lichfield Road, Dan?" asked Frank eagerly. Despite the naivety of the question, like asking a stranger from Birmingham if he knew Mrs Smith of Nechells, rather miraculously Dan *did* know Lichfield Road. He knew it because it was an arterial road in the north east of Birmingham and on the canal's line of approach into city. He responded to the continuing questions: the King Edward pub was at the start of Lichfield Road and was directly opposite to a main barge mooring. You looked out for the Navigation at Bromford, and then after the Cuckoo, the next big canal pub was King Edwards.

Anticipating the youngster's next question, Dan looked intently at his young friend while he told him, "Don't ask me to take you there Frank! I can't do it! It's against the law; they'd say it was kidnapping; I would finish up in Winson Green!"

Frank knew about Winson Green Prison: it was close to home and he had a very clear memory of one morning, when with his Mom he had listened to the morning news on Mrs Smith's precious radio. It was an occasion that everybody was aware of: the hanging of a murderer in Winson Green.

The radio took them outside the prison: it led them inescapably, by fearful talks with friends and family of the murderer, via descriptions of last meals traditionally eaten, of comforting visits by the prison's Padre, right up to – and through the deep and rich chimes of Big Ben – to nine o'clock.

As the first hour was solemnly tolled by the great clock there was an instant's gap in their lives. The gap was filled by the terrible image of a blind-folded man being launched into eternity. The trap door was released, and he was falling: dropping through the wooden hatch, with a hemp rope round his neck. There was a silence after the ninth hour was sounded, filled with their knowledge: they knew that a man was dead; hanging there with a broken neck.

Society's need for revenge was satisfied. The hanging, so graphically presented to a young mind by the radio, filled it with a vivid horror that would resurface now and again throughout a large part of his life.

Frank knew that he could never kill anybody: but what if he was hanged by mistake; what if they just *thought* that he had killed somebody? Winson Green was a nightmare to a young mind.

He did not ask Dan to take him to Birmingham, but he *did* ask him more questions, and when he left to walk back alone to the Harding's, Frank combined and alternated his deep breathing exercises with a litany of place names: Alrewas, Fradley Junction, the Swan, Coventry Canal, Fazeley, Birmingham canal, Navigation

197

pub, Cuckoo Bridge pub, King Edward pub, Lichfield Road, and HOME.

Frank had had a very good day: the interesting, wonderful barge, lovely people, new friends, and a glorious escape route in the planning. He allowed himself a rare smile as, still breathing deeply; he approached the cottage, and Mrs Harding.

His breathing exercise became a continuing rhythm folded into the newly learned place names: Alrewas, Fradley, Swan pub, Coventry Canal, Fazeley, Birmingham Canal, the Navigation pub, the Cuckoo Bridge, King Edward pub, the Lichfield Road, and HOME.

Chapter 29

At the next day's get-together of the Slummy Brummys, Frank told the gang of the barge he had been on; he related all the details of the great day that had thrilled him so much, and he shared his decision with them: he was going to run away.

Appropriately they had seen another barge on its way before the big plan was discussed in detail. With the departing boat on its purposeful way; taking its cargo and its all-together-family, on to another lock and another destination, Frank's intention to walk to his Birmingham home came under scrutiny. His embryo plan was little more than an intention, but it could be woven into their customary plotting and planning. Frank listened intently as Joe, Harry and Betty considered the problems that could arise from his running away.

First of all though, they decided, in turn, that the plan was for Frank alone. It was not for them. They had nothing to escape from, and nothing to escape to. For them the illusion of Birmingham, family, love, security, and the images which they had carried in their heads and hearts for so long had, on inspection faded away. The city dream had been supplanted by the village reality.

Betty knew now that she would stay here, for always. This was her chosen home, with chosen people. She would not search for a greater happiness than the one she had miraculously found.

Harry likewise had no inclination to go back to Birmingham: to a family that did not exist for him anymore. He liked living and working on the farm. Mr Jackson recently had told him that he was pleased with his work and had confirmed that there was a full-time job for him when he left school. He was not thought of as an evacuee, or as a lodger. He was no longer a useful lad to help out with the chores; he was not a casual farm worker: he was *family*. This was a new concept for the Jacksons as well as for Harry. They had no children and were too old to have any now, but in a recent long discussion with her husband Mrs Jackson had agreed that if a son *had* come to them, she would hope that he would have been like Harry.

Joe had the same reasons why he did not want or need to escape. In any event he *could not* leave. Isabel needed him. That was the main reason to stay, but now he had a job as well! In the evenings and weekends he worked for a new couple in the village: Chris and Emma Johnson. The Johnsons had taken on the garage business deserted by the Evans's.

The young couple had received him cordially when, shortly after their arrival Joe had visited and asked if there was any work he could do for them out of school hours. There was an enormous amount of work that he could do.

He had worked very hard all of the last Saturday and he laboured through Sunday afternoon as well. When Chris paid him they had chatted for a while, and Joe was told that he was doing a great job. The business needed him! It could do with all time he could spare them. The excited boy was told that he could make himself available for work at any time he wanted.

Joe's first task had been to scrape up, sweep and clear away all of the dirty oil that had invaded the premises. He made a good job of that, but first he replanted the big **'B'**. One day he would show Betty that letter in coal, where he had reset it, in the far corner of the rear garden.

The Johnsons were a newly married couple and newcomers to the county and the village. Chris who was apprentice trained in the motor business, had failed his medical for the Army with badly perforated eardrums. His father had supported him with cash when the garage and workshop business had been put up for sale by the bank. The place was offered at a very attractive price: reflecting how badly it had been neglected by the Evans men. The price paid by the Johnsons was just enough to clear the Evans debt owed to the bank. And now they had an assistant.

Chris and Emma had been pleased, and surprised, with Joe's performance. Joe was naturally happy and immediately comfortable with his new bosses and with the work. He was given the title of Assistant Mechanic – and it suited him well – he was going to be a full mechanic.

Feeling important and happy he had taken his first earnings home to Isabel. Since she had the baby, there was no early prospect of a job for *her* in the village, and with her husband gone she could only worry about money. The garage, the job and the money were all part of a hint of light on the horizon. Joe was keeping the glimmer alight.

Joe was needed here; he was happy with his new responsibilities; he did not need to escape; he did not want to escape. Frank had his enthusiastic backing and his conviction that it was the right thing to be planning, but he would not be going with him.

The youths from Birmingham realised that things had changed, and – at a rapid rate – they were continuing to change.

Many, perhaps most, of the children who had arrived with them at the beginning of the war had left by this time. They had been collected by relatives who were now convinced that the war would be won: the question was not *if* but *when* the war would be over. They were optimistic about the safety of the city, and confident of the protection they themselves could provide for the children. They were the parents who had missed their children. They could not abdicate responsibility for them. Indeed some children had been reclaimed by their families within a few days of their arrival: they were never evacuees.

The friends could see that their important meetings were important *childhood* meetings, and for the first time Frank became aware that he was a little 'out of age' with the others. He could contribute to all of the gossip; he could review school, church, family, village and war news. Now however – and suddenly it happened – the others had need to talk of jobs and responsibilities, and their lives were being dominated by these grown-up things.

There were different priorities now. It was no longer important to plan a 'scrumping' expedition, or talk about what to do about Brian; it was no longer exciting to chokingly share an acquired cigarette. It was time to realise that, with their improvised fishing lines, they would *never* catch a fish in the canal.

Now, although once again with their backs to the dilapidated wooden shed by the canal lock, they sensed that this could be their last *Slummy Brummie* assembly.

They did not have the time or the means to change the world with their planning. Without their interference the world was changing; they too were changing.

It was fast approaching the time for Frank to go, and time for his friends to stay.

Chapter 30

Sitting in the public bar of his local, Frank's father Bill Bourne was enjoying a pint of mild. It was the early evening shift at the King Edward and this was an unusual time for Bill to be there. More regularly now, as the bombing had eased off to nothing more than a continuing threat, he would have his pint in the later part of the evening; perhaps two pints if he was in funds from settlement of a painting job.

Today he was returning a long ladder that he had borrowed from Ted Hughes, an old mate who worked out of a small builder's yard across the road from the King Edward. The ladder was still lashed on Bill's high wheeled hand cart, pulled off the road at the side of the pub. Ted was not in the yard, but he knew Bill was coming and he would know where he would be waiting – where to find him, and his ladder.

Ted and Bill's friendship went back a long time, to a time before the Great War even, when as kids in the final year of school they met often at Nechell's Baths. It was there where they had learned how to swim and dive, and where they would 'bomb' likely looking, screaming girls, exchanging repartee and invitations to meet 'after'. Rarely would the invitations meet with success though; the girls were in inevitable, inseparable pairs and it was only occasionally that the twin hunters were able to match up with a like-minded couple at the Baths.

It was a tightly chaperoned society within the working class community of Aston and Nechells at that time; strict codes of behaviour were enforced, particularly by the matriarchs of the extended families that were the norm in those days. In protecting the girls they were safeguarding the family – nominally from shame, but more practically from the poverty of having to maintain: feed and clothe the additional offspring. The Grand-Dames exercised a dominant puritanical control of all things morally dangerous, taboo, or in any way to do with boy. Most dangers could be associated with the developing male animals.

But notwithstanding the close supervision, the rules, and the curfews, Bill and Ted had occasionally 'scored'. Success in scoring though was rarely more than some apologetic groping of a girl's well covered breasts, or a self-conscious kissing of clenched lips.

They had enjoyed growing up in the pre-war years: living through the months which were to be their curtailed youth in the months leading up to 1914.

Every Saturday of the football season they would meet at the Holt End of Villa Park. That was a man's place to be: standing in all weathers in noisy, jostling support of their great team – Aston Villa. Religiously they acclaimed their team at the three o'clock kick off. One Saturday it would be the First team; the following Saturday they would return at the same sacred time to watch the reserve team running out on to the pitch.

The lads lived in the shadows of the ground so they were able to comfortably walk to the Villa Park shrine. For them it was the amphitheatre for many unforgettable glories, and the scene of more than a few painful defeats.

Many thousands of Villa fans made the walking pilgrimage, while a great mass of the fans came by trams, which then lined up outside the ground to carry them efficiently back into real life after the game. Yet more thousands of fans cycled to the match. With fifty thousand or more supporters crowding the roads around the Park, the cyclists would necessarily have to push their machines through the one way tide of men. Push them and leave them in the trusted care of local householders. The fan would have a regular pitch, where he would leave his bike, week after week: securely stacked in the front garden of a terraced house backing onto the football ground. The bike's owner then moving to the next rituals of his day at the match: buying the penny programme which listed the players selected for both teams; queuing at the turnstile and winning access to his favourite spot on the terraces.

There to stand, in a crowd of similar flat capped or bowler hatted men. Those who sported hand knitted team scarves showed that fans of both teams were sharing the space. They shared information on which star players to watch in their respective sides; they exchanged good natured banter, and together shared the mounting anticipation. Perhaps they would splash out on a hot pie with their mug of Oxo at half time.

Win or lose the crowd lived and enjoyed the afternoon of ritual and committed skills. Then the War came, and the Game changed.

When Bill Bourne and Ted Hughes joined the queue to enlist at the Town Hall, both were under age, but, after a cursory medical examination both were nodded through. They joined with many other youths who collectively and proudly became known as the Warwickshire Bantams.

The two friends endured many months of slogging – digging and living embedded in mud and vermin in front line trenches – and together the two Villa supporters from Brum caught a whiff of German gas. In the immediate rear of the Front Line they recovered from their temporary blindness. Very quickly both of them were declared fit enough to re-enter the trenches.

There Bill was the first of the two friends to 'cop one'. On his first venture over the top after the gas attack a bullet slammed through his chest and into a lung.

After Bill had been dragged back into the trench from No Man's Land, Ted had seen his friend on a stretcher: apparently awaiting burial. Bill was dead! Ted was in a file of men moving to another section of the trench when he saw him. He gently touched

Bill's head as he passed. "Ta Ra Bill," he murmured as he moved on.

Neither man expected to see the other again. Bill had heard that Ted had been seriously wounded shortly after he had won his own bullet, but both men beat the odds; both survived. Survival: it was rather like breaking the rules.

Several months after the wars end, against the odds, the friends met again. Separately both men had gravitated to their usual place on the Holt End of Villa Park: the same spot where they had always met in the years before the War. Standing together – in a mainly pre-occupied and wordless partnership – they watched their beloved Aston Villa. It was a rare time of joy in those shameful post war days of no reward. They talked a lot that evening; they drank many pints of congratulatory, celebratory Mild beer.

They tried to live as normally as they had done in the years before the war came: they were back on their home territory after their foreign nightmare. They returned to the same local where – coincidentally, but nevertheless inevitably – they found each other again. They continued to use the pub, without thinking that this was so they could keep in touch – with each other – and with normality.

Both had married; both had kids; both continued to suffer from their wounds, and from the hellish memories. Together they had returned to experience an ungrateful country of inequalities.

With no sign of Ted, Bill finished his pint and left the pub with barely a nod to the barman. Wrestling his cart upright he laboured with its unwieldy loaded weight to get it moving. Gaining momentum he aimed the heavy cart, with its high wheels and long load, out of the pub's forecourt. With bloody minded purpose – ignoring the traffic, and the threatening foul language of the Lichfield Road – he manhandled the long load across the thoroughfare and onto the canal mooring yard. More sedately he continued across the yard to Ted's patch in the far corner.

His mate still had not arrived, and Bill wandered to the canal side. He sat on a mooring bollard, took the last Woodbine from a pack of five and crumbled the empty paper packet into the canal. Impassively he sat and smoked. Not seeing anything, but instinctively reacting when a barge eased alongside the wharf where he sat. The barge required to berth and needed the bollard that he sat on.

Out of his reverie; with his cigarette finished but still with no sign of Ted, Bill moved to where the barge's horse had moved. It had been released from the barge's tow rope, and had ambled across the yard. It now stood with its muzzle exploring some straggly weeds at the fence. It looked up with interest as the man approached. Bill took hold of its trailing harness, and stroked the intelligent head while murmuring his genuine admiration to the attentive beast.

His friend Ted arrived as Bill was fussing the animal, and at the same time as a young lad, having completed his task of mooring the barge came over with the horse's nose bag and a cheerful, "Thanks mate!"

The comrades moved away and unloaded the long ladder from Bill's handcart. They lodged this on its support brackets which were fitted on the fence at the back of Ted's small wooden shed. Without conversation they worked their way across the now busy Lichfield Road and into the public bar of the King Edward.

Bill bought two pints of mild beer and took these to the corner bench seat where Ted had settled. After a satisfying first draught they reverently placed their glasses on the small round table before Bill spoke.

"Thanks for the ladder Ted," he paused before continuing. "Don't reckon I will be using it again though … it nearly killed me this time. I haven't got the strength, or the bottle, for it now." He urgently sought a cloth from his trouser pocket and covered his mouth as he fought against a long phlegmy cough.

"I'm on the way out mate. The ladder work is killing me. Don't know what I can do though. I have to work outside. Even if they gave me a job I couldn't cope with a job in a factory." He laughed, "Or cope with all that money they're paying!"

Ted grinned, "We're going to the knacker's yard together friend!" He continued with a mock seriousness, "But do you think we could pull a couple of bints for one last time before we go?"

Bill's laugh at this preposterous idea brought on another paroxysm of coughing. He brought it under control before spluttering, "Never mind for one last time – let's pull a couple for the *first* time shall we!"

Ted grinned, and passed him a cigarette. "Have another coffin nail mate!" he invited.

When the pints were finished Bill rose and left his friend alone in the pub with a promise that he would return very shortly. He explained, "I've got to see our Ellie. I've heard that she's having more trouble with that sneaky little bugger she married. She lives just round the corner. I'll be back in ten minutes or so. You'll still be here, won't you?" He did not wait for a response, nor expect one.

Ted was not going anywhere. He set himself for a quiet evening: among like souls, in a sanctum of smoke, inconsequential chatter and mild beer. He ordered his second pint and smiled at the tall bargee who joining him at the bar, was waiting for service while Ted's pint was being pulled.

"Is that you just moored up over the road?" he asked companionably. The bargee nodded, introduced himself as Dan, and confirmed that he had moored up there just for the one night. With a nod towards the corner table Ted invited Dan to take a seat with him.   Their conversation ranged predictably far and wide: the war, rationing, the black market, the weather … evacuees. At this point Ted heard about the kid from Birmingham: the lad who had so impressed the bargee a couple of days earlier.

Dan confessed that he very rarely went into pubs but he had

made this visit particularly on the off-chance that someone would know of that unhappy kid in Roslington. He knew him only as Frank and although he had learned that this was Frank's home area, he was annoyed that he did not know the lad's second name. He could so easily have learned his surname.

Ted listened with avid interest then leaned towards Dan and confided, "My mate Bill has a boy Frank who's been evacuated – I don't know where, but Bill will be back soon. He will know where his lad is at. It's amazing … but you know, it could be the kid you're talking about."

He went on to explain to Dan that the Bournes were an unhappy and broken family. He shared his concern about Bill's health with his new friend. "He never got over the bullet in his lung: that collapsed with the bullet. Coming on top of the gassing it's just about wrecked him: it's given him no chance since the war."

Dan was listening intently and Ted continued, "I was lucky when I took my bullet – if you *can* be lucky with a bullet. It was in the muscle, and I was always getting better from it. Not like Bill's slug: that got hidden away inside him. And it's always festering – wrecking him. His family is wrecked by it and so is his working. He just can't cope with it. None of us were *lucky*, but Bill has had a bucketful of bad luck. He is a real unlucky sod. And he's a good bloke really – but after the war he was never well enough; he just couldn't earn enough – to support Gladys and the kids – and of course the kids just kept coming." Dan did not interrupt; he did not want to break the rhythm of Ted's monologue.

"Then," Ted said, "then, when she went to the Priests for help – for food and boots what they needed – all that he couldn't get for them, Bill just gave up. He's been my mate for ever – and always will be." Then he added sadly, "But its hard work to get a laugh out of him nowadays."

Chapter 31

It was well over an hour later that Bill returned to the King Edward. He was surprised to find that his friend was still in the bar, sitting alone at the corner table. Ted lifted himself out of his chair immediately he saw Bill coming into the bar. He went to the bar counter and returned with a pint for his friend.

Bill grunted his thanks before explaining his late return. "Ellie's in a right state," he told his friend, and elaborating, "The little toe-rag is back, and he's in the Nick again."

Ted was reminded of the near riot in Aston some three years ago. Following the big brawl at the Grapes, Bill's hooligan son-in-law had been charged, and soon afterwards found himself standing before magistrates. With little time to waste on this lost-cause of a man, the court had given him the choice of prison or immediate transfer from the police cells to the Army. Les had taken what appeared to be the obvious best option. Only too quickly did he realise that he had taken the wrong option – and it was an option of no return.

The Pioneer Corps and Les were not meant for each other. It was not for him, it was worse than prison. With considerable experience of 'volunteers' like Les they had set out to break him. They knew how to mould a thing like Les into a labouring soldier. They worked at the task for many months but he continued to disagree; he refused to conform and following yet another very long spell in the 'glasshouse' he had deserted.

"The stupid little bleeder frightened Ellie half to death. He just appeared in the back yard, about half an hour before the Redcaps showed up. He isn't the one-off he thinks he is and the MPs have sorted out dozens of washouts like Les. They went straight up to the attic! The daft prat got out onto the roof. They just let him stew there for a couple of hours …He was on show for all of Aston, the stupid little bastard!"

He sipped at his drink, accepted a cigarette, and after simmering down he said with quiet satisfaction, "When they *did* get him in they gave him a right pasting. Ellie doesn't know where they have taken him now, but – at last – I don't think she cares."

The two men sat with their thoughts and emotions. Their own experience, taken to the point of death, had left them with no love for the Army. They had suffered the harsh discipline; injustice; inequality; screaming sergeants; bullying corporals; arrogant posturing officers. They detested the Redcap police, but knew that they were necessary: they had to be there – to deal with Les. The two men were instinctive patriots. They *had* fought for King and Country: with much grumbling, but without analysis, and without question. Desertion was inexcusable, an unforgivable sin.

"How's Ellie when you left?" asked Ted. "Not good," was the answer, "She's looks bleeding awful. I reckon that she has never been right since she had that miscarriage, although the doctor always says she *will* be OK … she will never be OK while that runt is around her neck. I have got to do something, and do it quick. She has got to get away from that place. Les's Mom is giving her grief; blaming her for everything! She is a worker is our Ellie, and with him out of the way, she WILL be alright."

He went on to explain his thinking to his friend, "There's a two-bed flat come empty in the house I'm in on Gravelly Hill. I've only got a room there, but I reckon I can get that flat. I shall go after it tomorrow – I've always been on time with rent and we will be able to manage the bigger rent. With what I can still earn, and … when she's better …" He paused, "We'll manage. I'm buggered if I know what else I *can* do."

211

He turned to talk directly to his one true friend, "You have done better than me with your life Ted. With Ethel, and with your kids. I know I've been a washout! All I ever do is tread water – I just survive one day – so that I can live another day. I'm sick of it – but I *will* get Ellie out of this. I will be a dad … to at least one of my kids."

Ted started to tell his friend about his discussion with Dan and the evacuee boy whom the bargee had met on his recent travel. Dan returned to the Pub as he was speaking. He had come back to meet with Bill, and without getting a drink for himself, he joined the two men at their table.

He repeated to Bill all that earlier he had told his friend; he recounted his meeting with Frank at Roslington, two days previously.

Bill felt for the postcard which Ellie had just given him: the forgotten, lost, and only recently found, crumbled old postcard. The card with the address.

Chapter 32

The scene for his comeuppance was inadvertently chosen by Brian himself that Saturday afternoon. He had left the house and was waiting on the canal bridge for his gang associates to join him. This hump backed bridge, no more than fifty yards from the rear of his house, gave access only to fields. It was rarely used by the farmer and was a convenient and regular meeting place for him and his gang. Brian was not *looking* for Frank, but from his elevated vantage point, and by accident, he spotted him. His chosen enemy was a long way away, but even from this distance it was unmistakably Frank. Brian could see that he was alone by the distant lock.

The evacuee was alone by the lock. He was set up to become the adventure of the day, his victim of choice.

Brian set off, aping his current cinema hero and adopting the classical Tarzan tracking style. The hawthorn hedge grew alongside most of the towpath in the area, and by keeping low behind it he was able to work his way unseen up to the canal lock. Brian had spied Frank here before; he knew it was a favourite place for the evacuee and his mates, but today Frank was alone, and preoccupied.

Frank had been there for some time. Most of that time he had day dreamed, preoccupied by the idea of running away. He had mooched about in the broken down shed; had thrown a few stones into the canal, and had thought about fishing.

No arrangement had been made to meet with his friends and he did not expect to see them today: they were all so grown up and busy. Finally he decided to have another go at the fishing. This was inspired by the discovery, during his mooching among the debris in the hut, of a fish hook and a jumble of discarded fishing line. It had been left there by sheltering fishermen in the past; it sparked this good idea. He was at a loose end and doing nothing else in any case.

He made a fishing line from the discarded line, farm twine, a simple twig float, the hook, and many, many knots. He completed the unsophisticated fishing tackle by lashing the well knotted line to the end of a five foot long wooden lath. This had been sacrificed by the dilapidated canal-side shed: it was easily levered off the inside wall. The ancient muck heap in the allotment contributed a heavy healthy earthworm, and with this impaled on his make shift gear Frank began his fishing exercise.

He manoeuvred with care across the foot wide wooden ledge which was fitted to one side of the lock gate. He used one hand to carry his fishing rod while with the other he held on to the low handrail of the lock gate.

The agile barge people: men, women, and children regularly ran across these narrow ledges. The walkways were fitted to every one of the lock gates they met during their day, and they traversed them with familiarity. The youngsters from the barges saw no danger, and so they raced with no regard for it. The sluice paddles controlling the water level were installed on both sides of the canal at the lock entrance. To operate the paddles – to raise or lower the water level in the lock – the barge people had to hurtle from one side of the canal to the other. There was nothing tentative about *their* use of the precarious footway; the barge youngsters were not even aware of the safety handrail.

The evacuees were becoming equally adept, and occasionally they competed to see who could take the least steps, the fewest flying leaps to get from one bank to the other. Today Frank had eased himself more carefully along the ledge, taking hold of the rail, more to safeguard his precious hooked worm than for his own safety.

When he was above the centre line of the canal he parked himself. This was where the big fish would be. From the canal bank they were out of range of his casting, but here they were under his rod end. Nursing his cumbersome fishing gear, he perched and decided on which side of the gate to invest his worm. He chose to cast first into the lock itself.

Both end gates of the lock were closed, so the water level was at its highest, but it was still about four feet below his dangling feet. It took him less than five minutes to decide that there were no fish trapped within the lock. So he re-adjusted his position, turning around to be able to fish on the other side. Here he was going to catch the big ones that obviously did not want to go into the lock. He reasoned that the big ones would not rely on food being trapped within a confined brick built lock. Logically they would expect food in the canal proper. That was where his worm dinner was waiting for their attention.

The handrail was on this side and Frank was able to comfortably brace his knees against it as he fished.

There had been no barge traffic at all since his arrival: a rare idle day for the canal. Frank wondered if the barge families had Saturdays and Sundays off from work; did they have weekends like ordinary people? Anyway, with no one needing to open and shut the lock gates today he could site himself on the gate itself, and there was a good chance that he would not be interrupted. He had no arrangement to meet with his chums that afternoon; they were not getting together so often nowadays. But often somehow, they found each other's company, and he hoped that someone might turn up.

Brian's sudden yelling, and triumphant appearance at the lock side startled Frank. It made him jump, and he grabbed at the handrail by his knees. He had avoided this encounter for a long time, but knowing all the time that it was inevitable. He looked down the towpath, hoping for sign of Harry or Joe – a barge perhaps – or anyone!

"You have been well hidden just lately you catholic bastard," called Brian, "Ain't you lucky I came along … to make your day more interesting?" He was standing at the end of the lock gate, looking huge, and leaving no escape for his victim.

Frank knew immediately that he was trapped. If he ran across the ledge to the side furthest away from his tormentor, he would then have to run the length of the lock before he could get up to and across the adjacent bridge. He *had* to get on to the towpath side, the side where Brian was: there was no path or access, or escape through the hedges and fields on this side of the canal. But if he chose the bridge route to attempt escape, Brian had far less distance to run; he would get to the bridge much more quickly than he could.

The only other option, only it wasn't an option, was to walk across the lock gate: into the arms of the waiting bully. There to take his beating, or there to take him on.

He assessed once more the distance he would have in which to outpace the bigger boy.

"Don't even think about it," shouted Brian. "You're in the shit mate! Come and take your medicine … You never know – I might *not* throw you in if you come nice and quiet like. I might just sit on your head … and shit in your poxy face."

Again Frank considered the alternatives: he could stay where he was, and hope that a barge would come into view before Brian killed him. But there was no sign of barges, either up or down the canal. He could stay where he was and wait for Brian to come after him. Perhaps he could push *him* in the cut. That was probably his best option. It *could* give him a chance to somehow trip or at least try to get the bully off balance, turn the tables and get *him* in the water. Or he could walk off the lock gate and have a go against the mighty Brian. Was that an option? When he knew that the oversize bugger would slaughter him!

All of his options disappeared however when the first stone, accurately thrown by Brian, hit him on the side of his head. Brian yelled in triumph. The second and third stones missed him, but the next missile smashed into the hand he had instinctively raised to protect his face. Frank knew that he had to leave his precarious perch: he had to face the screeching bully. He had to meet him in a no hope fight.

Brian, looking around to check that there was no one to witness the villainy he planned, erupted into triumphant yelling when he saw that a couple of his gang were making their way down the towpath. He was cock-a-hoop. He did not need their help to pulverise this toe-rag, but he loved a supporting audience.

Gloatingly he shouted, "Come on Frankie, give yourself a chance. I might not kill you, you WILL get wet though! You have got to get wet. Course you have; when you go into the cut it will wash off the blood. And you can tell mom … you can tell MY mom Frankie… that Brian – *that's me* – picked up an ugly catholic turd of shit – *that's you,* and washed it off in the cut. You could ……"

His harangue was cut short by a quiet yet menacing voice from behind him. "You *have* got some interesting ideas Brian," voiced Joe. "Let's have some more mate. Harry and me, we're looking for ideas; that's because we're not quite sure what our Frank's got in mind for YOU!"

Joe and Harry had appeared from the opposite direction that Brian had approached from, and they had used the same tactics that he had. From a distance they had seen their friend in his precarious position, and using the hedgerow as cover they had moved quickly, to appear through the same gap in the hedge that Brian had used earlier. He had been too engrossed to spot them, and now he was trapped.

Despairingly he saw that his gang had assessed the changed situation and were melting away down the further towpath. In the time it took for him to despairingly pray for his gang's support, he found that Frank had taken the initiative. He was now standing close behind him, blocking any escape in that direction; and Frank looked different. Standing there, immoveable, he looked bigger, much bigger than the insignificant Frank – the target he had been goading and hurling stones at only a couple of minutes ago.

The young Frank had evacuated the lock gate, leaving his fishing apparatus where it fell. He had crossed the gate and had run the route that he had earlier discounted, along the lock, and across the bridge, to come up behind the erstwhile master of the situation.

"Ain't it just a more interesting day than you thought Brian? Can it get any more interesting than this?" Frank could not keep the excitement out of his voice and the question was voiced in a high pitch. Aware that he was practically squeaking, he corrected himself and continued in a more normal conversational, adult tone.

He pleasantly suggested, "I think you have met my mate Harry, and my mate Joe: we're the Slummy Brummys – you may have heard about us?" Brian certainly knew about the Brummys. But always on previous encounters an escape route had been open to him; hitherto he had been able to avoid close confrontation. Today he was alone – and there was no escape route.

"I was only joking Frank!" he whined. "I wasn't going to do nothing!" Stung and triggered by that whinging lie, Frank screamed loudly, *"Well I ain't joking!"* and with startling intensity, and uncharacteristic ferocity he attacked the much bigger youth.

All the frustrations of the past couple of years: the humiliations, the punches and kicks, the branding on his leg, the indelible scarring of his mind – all that had been carved by Brian, and his mother Mrs Harding; Sister Alice; the war – compelled him to hit and hit, and hurt and hurt.

He punched and kicked and manhandled Brian to the ground. Sitting on his chest he repeatedly punched and lambasted him. Much of his effort was ineffective: neither drawing blood, breaking bones nor raising bruises, but it was nevertheless a wonderful frenzied, cathartic retribution. Almost as satisfying for Joe and Harry to see as it was for Frank to inflict. Brian cowered from the enraged attack. He could do nothing other than curl up, protect his belly and face – and blubber. Frank, with the uninvited image of Mrs Harding in his head, kept on hammering; he was hitting her son, and he was hitting her.

He grunted a litany of grievances in loose rhythm with his blows – "Burn me! Brand me!" he landed a particularly hard punch on Brian's forehead as he shouted, "Drown me would you? ... Have all the sweet ration points! ... Piddle in the bath! ... Give the Beano away; burn it so I can't read it! ......"

He paused as though searching for more cardinal sins to expose, but then he murmured, "I am *better* than you Brian! I ain't frightened of you ... And I ain't scared of your mom neither." With one last, and blood-letting blow to Brian's mouth Frank rolled off the whimpering bully.

His friends moved towards where they both lay on the towpath, one lying in ignominy and the dust, and their friend in the glory of his battlefield.

"I think that goes without saying son. You are a lot better than he will ever be," said Harry. Without any objection or resistance he took Frank's hand and pulled him to his feet.

Joe joined in the congratulations, pounding Frank's back in his excitement. "That was shit hot mate! You couldn't have done it better," adding, "Though you *could* have done it sooner – the little arsehole was no match for you, and never has been in my opinion." He went on, "But we have still got the little matter of this bastard branding you Frank. I reckon we should have a trial and find him guilty and hang him, or something!"

Brian was terrified to hear these words, aimed in his direction by Joe, and more terrified to see Big Harry nodding in agreement. He stopped howling: which was in any case more for effect than in any reaction to pain. Now he searched wildly about him, before again focussing his staring terrified eyes on the avengers. They deliberated his future: he contemplated the lack of it.

The impasse ended when Frank spotted a barge rounding the far bend of the canal. Without discussion the two older boys grabbed

Brian and manhandled him to the obvious and only place they could take him: the old wooden shed. Inside it he was shoved into a corner away from the door. Joe cast around the litter searching for something with which to restrain the prisoner. His sole reward was an ancient hessian sack. Frank remembering his improvised fishing rod ran back to the lock and recovered most of the tackle from the footway ledge where he had dropped it in his earlier panic.

The fishing hook had wedged itself in the gap at the back of the wooden pathway. He could not dislodge the hook and the old fishing line and he abandoned them. He was able though to break free the wooden rod and with it the heavier twine.

Returning to the shed with these he found that Brian had been gagged with a filthy strip of sacking torn from the old potato bag. Joe, standing over the cowed prisoner was threatening him with all sorts of consequences should he dare to move or make any sound.

Harry claimed the twine from Frank's defunct fishing rod. He was always looking for something to cut or shape with his recently acquired clasp knife. He produced this treasure, a surprise gift from Mr Jackson, and with a flourish cut the twine free. With it Brian was securely bound hands and feet.

They could hear the lock being operated, the gates being opened, and the barge easing into the lock. They translated the noises they heard into the entry gates being closed behind the barge; the sluices opened to lower the lock water to match the canal level below. They knew the tow line had been unhitched from the centre-line towing spar that was fitted towards the middle of the barge. They heard the horse plodding down the path. They visualised it standing patiently, waiting for the line to be passed under the bridge. They knew it had been reconnected to the barge when they heard the lower gates being opened to their full width. All this they heard, and saw clearly in their mind's eye, as they stood or squatted in their shelter; with one only of them praying for discovery. The noises died away with the routine passing of the barge.

Returning to the day's business, the three evacuees deliberated on their next move. Brian struggled to get free. He hurt his wrists by this futile wrestling with the twine, which tightened with each struggle. The improvised gag was torturing him as it became sodden with his tears and unrestrained snot. Frank saw that he was choking and eased the gag off giving an immediate relief.

"Any row from you Brian and it's back on – only tighter, and more of it will be stuffed inside your gob!" he hissed with uncommon sadism. For the first time he was in charge of the Brian and Frank relationship. He had *beaten* the bane of his existence; he relished the difference in his life, he could taste it. An hour ago he was stranded and at the mercy of the tyrant, a bit of luck and a scrap later – an impetuous challenge and fight – and his life was changed.

Albeit with tremendous support from Joe and Harry; but it had been moral support – *they* hadn't beaten Brian – *he* had: For the first time in his life *Frank Bourne had won a battle!*

On impulse he tweaked Brian's nose. "How does that feel," he asked, mimicking Brian's typical mischief of just yesterday. "I'm just checking to see if it's on tight enough." This was a regular torment he had suffered from his captive. It was also a regular trick of his mother, Mrs Harding. Strangely Frank got little satisfaction from the childish retribution. He was not a natural bully as Brian was. He knew that anything the three of them did together would not be life threatening; but Brian did not know that. He moaned pathetically as he listened to the stage whispered considerations of the evacuees.

"We have got to get the fire going," Joe turned to Harry, "Have you brought the matches?" Harry had matches that he kept in a small tobacco tin. On the farm he always volunteered to start any fire that was necessary, and he could always be trusted to have the matches to hand.

Joe left the shed promising, "I'll get a good 'un going in a couple of ticks," and inviting the others to sort out something to heat up. "Something iron and heavy – we will want the scarring to show up like."

It could only mean that a branding was in the offing. Brian rolled his eyes and groaned loudly enough for Harry to threaten him with the gagging sack, hinting, "There's enough of the potato sack left; it would just about cover your whole bloody head Brian, even though it might suffocate you of course."

The victim pleaded, "Please Harry .. Please stop. You can't keep on .. I'm sorry what happened to Frank .. I done wrong. But it'll never happen again. I promise."

Harry responded to the plea with an enigmatic, "You're bloody right there mate. It will never happen again." He continued with the softening up of Brian Harding. "But you're a menace and I reckon that *if*, and I say *if*, we let you get away from here *alive*, you'll race back to your Mom, and our Frank will be in it up to his neck again." Brian begged again for them to let him go; he vowed that he wouldn't tell, not ever!

They ignored him but instead continued to discuss the fascinating options ahead of them. These ranged from some very rude ones, like pinching his trousers and running him through the village, and/or, tying him naked onto one of the pit ponies, and setting that loose. But branding was favoured. The evacuees felt that this was *just* and right. Also Brian would always have something to remind him of why he was being *so good all the time*. "It would remind you why you stopped being a bully and a thug – wouldn't it?"

Joe re-entered to report that the fire was OK. It was clear that Joe also approved of branding; however he needed some more dry wood to help make it happen. They sorted out a sizeable amount from within the derelict shed, and Joe happily returned to his duties claiming, "Nearly ready, and I've found a big iron spanner thing. It'll make a lovely burn when you get that red hot. I reckon we should brand him on his bum to start with. The iron thingy is big enough even for his fat arse, but we need another spot to scorch with it: it has to be someplace where he can look at it all the time."

"That iron thingy is a lock key spanner," said Harry. "If you use *that* on Brian's arse then no bargee is going to be able to use it afterwards. Urgh! You'll ruin it. Can't we find something a bit less useful to brand him with?"

Frank had picked up a long nail from the shed's floor, and he could see two or three others lying about. He suggested, "If we got these nails *very* hot, and if we tied him down *very* tightly, and turned him over on to his belly, we could drop these on his bum ... We could even make a pattern with them ... like a proper cowboy brand." They all, except Brian, thought that this was a marvellous idea. He continued his grovelling.

"Oh shut up Brian," ordered Harry. "Shut up unless you've got any *better* ideas?"

"I've got a good one," shouted Joe with more than his normal mischief. "You remember the pig when they lifted it up in the air – we could lift Brian like that! As high as you like: he'd have to be upside down, his legs up, of course. Then you can get at him easy like." Then Joe, conversationally went on to ask, "But do we *want* to cut Brian's throat?" The friends considered this, but the question was left hanging in the air, left unanswered.

Without saying a word, Harry took the last of their line and fastened this securely around the binding already on Brian's ankles. He looked up for a secure mounting point in the roof space of the shed. Nothing looked very robust. Joe and Frank entered into the spirit of this new idea and together they noisily selected the strongest looking timber. Harry, with his arms round Frank's legs raised him into the air, just high enough so that he could pass the end of the line over the chosen spar.

Brian was frantic now as the significance of his likely fate hit him; Harry rearranged the gag to stifle his screaming. The boys then lifted his lower half and hoisted on the line. When the slack in the line was taken up, and although his back was still on the floor, Brian's boots were nearly three feet above it. He was terrified, and looking very uncomfortable in his terror. Using the lock key the boys had been able to hammer four of the large nails into the side of the shed, and to these they untidily secured the line. "We can get him right up into the air later – that's when we're ready for him – to be right up in the air – upside down," volunteered Joe helpfully, and he shouted at the unfortunate youth, trussed, partly suspended and helpless, "And you should lose some of that fat on you Brian. You don't make it easy for us you know – what with all that weight."

Three of the four boys in the shed laughed, and Joe went on, "And you're not only fat … You're bloody noisy Brian. You can dish it out alright, but you can't take it can you? Frank has given you a pasting today. You didn't like that at all did you?"

Harry took over the hectoring, debating, "And if … I say *if…* you get out of this alive, I wonder if you will remember how it felt; what it was like being pasted?" Brian was gurgling, and Harry eased the gag away, easing his panic, but threatening to put it back as soon as he made any sort of noise.

By unspoken agreement the three lads went outside. They moved away from the shed, away from Brian's hearing. They had to settle on their next moves and they did not find that easy. After all their recent discussions of this very matter they found themselves entirely out of ideas. The sight of the gibbering beaten boy in his humiliating position had tempered their anger.

Frank was the first to comment. "I know he won't change, and I know that he'll scream it all out to his Mom that I've beaten him up." He paused before looking at his chums for confirmation, "But I *have* beaten him …haven't I? And I beat him square. You didn't have to help me thump him, did you? I gave him a scrap, *and I beat him!*" They were quick to agree with him: he *had* beaten the bully. Brian had been unbeaten until now. They talked of it for some time and Frank relived the fight blow by blow, even finding scraped damage on his fists that he reckoned came from Brian's face and head. Joe and Harry studied the evidence and had to agree with their proud mate. They also noted that Brian only started fights that he knew he would win: that's why he was unbeaten.

Harry spoke to Frank directly, "You did exactly the right thing starting that scrap, Nipper, and you did even more exactly right by finishing it!" This was a great tribute from Harry, he rarely put so many words together in one sentence – or indeed in an entire conversation.

They were aware that the afternoon was passing, and because of their activity it was passing more quickly than was normal.

Frank sobered them all by telling them that today had been declared bath day. He had to get back soon or all hell would erupt. "Brian could get away with being late," he said, "but I will get slaughtered. As well as drowned." He solemnly addressed his friends, "This is the last time. I won't be here for the next bath day. I should get on my way right now really. But I'm not quite ready. I have to get some stuff first."

Harry still had an hour or so before the evening milking, and Joe was alright with the time, although he said that he didn't want to be late home. It sounded as though Isabel had need of him today.

There was no further humiliation to pile on to Brian. They had had enough, and certainly, they agreed, *he* had had enough. Frank did not want to return to the Harding's and to the dreaded bath time, at the same time as the bully would return: Brian would be in a state and howling out for his mom to get revenge.

This was understandable, and it was settled that they would leave Brian where he was, perhaps lowering his feet down, just a little, into a more comfortable elevation, but leave him tied up and with the line left secured to their nails in the wall.

Joe accepted the job of releasing the prisoner, promising to return about six o'clock in the early evening. It would be safe to let him go then. Frank's bath would be over and if he had not left the village by then he could at least be prepared for the bully's return.

They were almost gentle with Brian as they manoeuvred his tied-up body into a more comfortable posture, but he howled and sobbed loudly when Joe, seeing the giveaway stain on Brian's short trousers shouted, "You've piddled yourself you fat pissy-arsed sod!"

225

He gave himself time for better effect, and then added solemnly, "We had planned to let you go, but now you can stay here. You must stay here while we decide how," and in a passable, indeed unmistakable Sister Alice mimicry, "you have to be *corrected*!" and he added, "you little Tyke!" The *Brummys* laughed; Brian sobbed.

With what was left of the door wedged back into its shut position the friends left, but after a few yards Frank stopped. Brian was making a row: the noise made by a terrified prisoner in contortions attempting to ease his bonds. After a short deliberation Frank returned quickly and eased himself back into the darkened shed. He carefully replaced and readjusted the gag to muffle the continuing sobbing. As he did this he spoke soothingly to the prisoner, "You behave Brian, and you'll be let go from here quite soon – that's if you behave of course. Stop throwing yourself about, you'll only make it worse and it'll hurt more. I promise that you will be alright quite soon. That's if you behave, and if you just shut up. Think about what you were going to do to me; then think about what I *did* do to you!"

Brian had calmed down as Frank spoke, but he whined again and struggled against the knots as he was reminded, "Did you know its bath day today Brian? I will make sure that you are in time for the bath." Frank went on to further reassure him, "But don't fret about it. Don't be worried that you won't be there on time. I suppose that I will have to go in the bath and take your turn." Then cheerfully he added, "I'll make sure that I piddle in the water before I get out – just for you mate!"

On the point of leaving Frank confided, "Joe is coming back later on. If you've been good he'll let you go. It won't be long … then you can run home to Mummy … and have your bath." Frank continued, following this promise of release with an ominous threat, "If you tell your mom anything about this I'm going to do you again Brian. Me and Harry and Joe will sort you out proper like. And you *will* get branded – and worse Brian! You will get very hurt! Ever so hurt!"

Frank left after resetting the door in its broken frame. Setting off again he saw that his friends, his co-conspirators, were watching him from some distance away. He waved that all was well, and received their salutes in return.

Chapter 33

After imprisoning Brian, Harry and Joe had not walked very far when they heard Frank levering the shed door open. They turned in time to see him re-enter the shed, and wondered what he might be doing. They considered returning themselves, but when he was seen to come out of Brian's prison and back on to the towpath, they merely exchanged farewell waves with him. Frank set off walking in the opposite direction to his friends.

'How much can happen in just one day?' Frank mused as he walked towards the Harding's. He knew that he was walking towards the worst part of the twenty four hours. He stopped for a short time at the lock, looking at its massive gates holding back the water and listening to the incessant noise of water escaping through gaps in the gates and in the sluice valves. Passing on he thought again about the fight, reliving it in detail and enjoying the memory of it.

Quickly however he felt compelled to stop the day dreaming, and he faced the reality that he was walking back to: the reality was Mrs Harding. He now he had to endure the bath and the drowning ritual that was the reality.

He practised his deep breathing as he walked. He filled his lungs, held his breath, and then slowly breathed out – allowing a gradual escape of spent breath – before the inevitable need to give up; with each exercise ending in a gasping relief as he breathed again.

Not entirely certain that he had mastered the technique that would save his life, he again exercised his lungs. He visualised doing this in the bath; under the dirty, several times used, bath water. Frank forced himself to think that very soon now he would be doing this for real. Fearfully he anticipated the events to come; doing this deep breathing for real, doing this tonight.

It was tempting to consider turning away, and running away right now. Why risk the drowning? But he had to collect his things, and if he could wait until they had gone to bed, if he could get out of the house unnoticed, there was a chance that the night hours would pass before the alarm was raised. Once that happened they would start to hunt him down. He calmed the panic that engulfed him at the thought of being hunted. It hit him again that it would be tonight, very soon now he would find out if his plan worked.

Could he survive the Harding's aggression twice in one day? Could he *beat* them twice in one day? Yes! He was sure that he could. Blimey, there was going to be an awful scene when darling Brian didn't show for his bath time. But with the water poured and the other baths taken he could not believe or hope that Mrs Harding would cancel *his* bath. She would not waste the water, and he knew that she would not want to miss out on her terrible game – with him.

He thought about Joe releasing Brian, and again he anticipated the inevitable mayhem that would be unleashed when Brian returned to the house. The terrified Brian in the shed would not be a terrified Brian then, not when he was safe with his mother. In an instant he would forget the Brummy threats, and promises of retribution.

Frank knew this. He had to think! He had to be prepared for when it happened, for it surely would happen. But what could he do – other than hide, or disappear, or run away! There was no choice – he had to run away! He had to run away before Brian was released and had chance to tell his mom all about it!

Earlier in the day, when Brian had been humbled by the battling Frank, Joe had colourfully described to him the scene when Mrs Harding found out about it. He forecasted that she would go 'ape shit'!

Despite his nervousness of the approaching nemesis, and ignoring his scared, liquefied guts and weakened limbs, Frank allowed a tiny chortle to percolate through his apprehension. Joe was so – 'ape shit right'.

A short time after leaving the shed Harry cut off across the fields to the farm, and Joe carried on walking towards his home with Isabel. Both their routes were in the opposite direction to that taken by their friend Frank.

Joe reflected on the day which was ending with Brian shut up and humbled in the canal side shed. Less happily he thought of his young mate walking towards bath night, and the other problems of the Harding's billet. To give Frank more time he resolved to release Brian no earlier than arranged. Meanwhile *he* was heading back to the warmth and comfort of Isabel's home. Izzy would have been busy today he thought. Izzy was his affectionate nickname for Isabel. He thought of the warm kitchen and anticipated his welcome into it. Probably toast and jam tonight, and possibly, if she had managed to get flour and stuff she would have baked and there would be scones. But as he approached the house he could see, and sense, that all was not well.

The drawn curtains confirmed this, and he found that the back door was locked. This door was *always* on the latch, always allowing free passage in and out of the house, from breakfast to bedtime. He had to knock on the door. He knocked hard, and the panic rising in him forced him to knock again – and again.

Then, pre-empting a third knock, the door opened, and Isabel was there! She turned away without a sound, and moving back she let him into the front room. Clearly distraught, she stood silently hugging her well-worn dressing gown tightly around her. She had been crying. Joe threw the door closed; swiftly moved to his friend, and naturally put his arms around her.

"What is it Isabel?" and without waiting for her to answer, "Its John ain't it?" She nodded and then collapsed against him, her body shuddering with suffocated sobs. Then the pressure was released as she could no longer hold on to her stifled anguish, and Isabel wailed.

It was some time before the keening and then the sobbing that followed subsided. They moved apart, and Joe taking her hand, led the worn out, shuffling young mother into the kitchen. With no discussion Isabel sat at the table. Joe made a pot of tea. Nothing was said. It was some time later that they talked: more exactly Isabel talked and the youngster listened.

Joe knew that she had not heard from her husband for several weeks. John always wrote whenever he could; although for a long time now she would only ever receive postcards. The cards were always heavily censored, and they told her nothing, other than to confirm and so comfort her that he was alive. Then the mail dried up entirely.

The postman waved to Isabel, but unfailingly after that acknowledgement he had to shake his head as he passed on his twice daily rounds. She waited for him every day, at first standing by the open front door, then looking out from behind the window curtains. She waited with bright hope for the postman. Then with each forlorn following of his passing, the bright hope dimmed slightly. Each wave, each shake of the head, and each passing, building until she *knew*. Then she watched no more: she willed the postman NOT to stop.

She knew John was in North Africa, and from the news on the radio and talk with villagers she had guessed that he was probably in a place called Tobruk. It sounded as though the British troops were safely entrenched there.

A telegram today regretfully informed her that he had been killed. No details with which to feed her grief, or ease her anguish: just baldly typed regrets that her husband, her man, had been killed.

231

"Oh Joe," she pleaded through her fresh tears, "How can we manage without John? What am I to do? What can I do?" The young lad wanted desperately to help her. He tried to share her broken heart; tried to comfort her, but found that you cannot take a part of, or a half of a broken heart.

Isabel often talked of John, but Joe had never met him. He knew only that he was away at the war, and hence by being away, he was not there with them, and he had no presence in Joe's life. If he *ever* had thought of Isabel's man it had been triggered by some comment or reminiscence voiced by her, something that only fleetingly entered into his day. His imagination only allowed him to think generically, of *all* the men in the Army, and the Navy and the Air Force. All the men were fighting, shooting, killing: all just winning the War. He had not thought of any of their side dying – and by dying, upsetting friends like Isabel.

He thought about the Custard Pie Roadman and recalled his quiet, reasoned philosophy, but he did not mention this to the quietly weeping Isabel.

Joe made more tea, and when young James cried from his cot upstairs he was easily able to get to the stairs ahead of Isabel. He was able to soothe and settle the infant: it was a happy daily task that he enjoyed and did well. When this was achieved he looked fondly at the sleeping baby and had a profound thought: 'Not yet three, and – just like Joe – James's got no dad.' Returning to the kitchen Joe found a quiet, exhausted woman.

They sat and talked through the hours. In the late evening Joe's stomach caught up with him and he was reminded of how very hungry he was. Clumsily he hacked out a doorstep of bread; added some more carefully sliced cheese, and topped it with Daddies brown sauce. With this they drank more tea. Joe insisted that the sandwich *had* to be shared; he would not eat any more than Izzy ate. She nibbled half-heartedly trying to comply with this instruction, and Joe made a game of it, ostentatiously matching nibble with nibble even managing to raise a wan smile at one stage.

Eventually it was agreed that she had eaten just as much of the sandwich as he himself had. Their evening meal, eaten at the nibbling pace was slow in passing.

James demanded more attention but he was soon resettled, and his mother, joining them in the room, gazed down at her son for a long time. She then lay down on the bed that was beside the cot, and she studied her tiny son's face through the cot bars. Finally she closed her eyes and at her unspoken invitation Joe stretched out beside her: he lay motionless, and then gently he took and held her hand. Isabel slept: totally spent, but comforted. After a short time Joe too fell into sleep.

All problems of the other world were swamped by this exhaustion he shared with Izzy. He had completely forgotten about the prisoner Brian.

James stirred in his cot, reacting with a baby's grumble to the feeble light of the dawn fighting the curtains. Isabel fought against wakening and barely moved at all but, sensing James's movements Joe was instinctively wide awake. He found that he was lying close alongside Isabel with his arm draped protectively over her.

They had slept, in their clothes on the top of the bed, their closeness keeping them warm, and the coldness of the night keeping them close. Isabel, holding his protective arm closely around her turned gently towards him, and she attempted a smile.

Then in an awful flash Joe remembered everything: Isabel's man, his friends Frank, Harry, the shed – Brian!

He leapt from his place on the bed and decided that he had not enough time to explain everything to Isabel. He was conscious of the awakening infant and so he leaned towards Isabel to whisper, "I've got to rush off now – but I will be back very quickly Isabel."

She again smiled at him and reaching out with her hand gently touched his face, and then pulled his head towards her. She kissed the top of his head and the side of his face. She kissed him softly before saying, "Thanks. Thanks for being here Joe."

Then she recalled the day they were in and reminded him, "There's no school today Joe, why all the hurry? Silly Joe."

He saw then the anguish of her grief suddenly reappearing. It showed in her eyes, and he desperately did not want to leave her. *But he had to leave.*

"I'm not going to school – but I do have to go – but only for a few minutes," he said, and added, "You feed James, and get some breakfast. I'll be back soon. I'll be back before you have had time to make us a cup of tea."

In the weak sun of the early morning Joe ran quickly to the canal and the lock side shed. The door, hanging on its one hinge gaped onto an empty interior. Brian had escaped … or Frank had come back to let him go, or … somebody had heard him whining and had released him. His mind raced with the possibilities.

He forced himself to reason it out. There was no sign of blood and he rationalized that Brian had *not died*. His vivid imagination pictured a bear sniffing for him, finding him, and dragging him away, or a fox – and he giggled – or a chicken. No – he was certain that Brian was still alive.

But what about Frank? If Brian was alive he would be back at home now and his mom would know about everything. His giggling stopped with the knowledge that if that was so … then it was Frank who was dead!

He searched outside the shed, looking for clues, for some indication of what had happened. There was nothing to inform him. He ran over to the bridge that humped its back over the canal. There was no sign of life in any direction. Nothing: nothing was moving either up or down the canal. He could find no explanation of anything.

In the canal? Joe did not look there; and neither did he look *in* the lock. He looked across, and up and down the canal and the lock; all was serene and without clues for him. He did not see the lifeless body *in* the lock. It was in suspense, floating just below the surface of the turgid canal water. It was in the lock: the huge bath which was the lock.

Chapter 34

In the early morning as Joe was searching – and even worrying about him – Brian was at his Gran's house.

Gran was cooking his breakfast, and after a weird and noisy night she was letting the unusually silent boy, know that she was in a foul mood. She could swear that she had not slept a minute. It was easy to blame Edna, and she grumbled out loud that her daughter never did anything proper like.

For some reason, late in the previous evening, Edna had left the grizzling boy – and his usual snotty nose – at her house. Without entering the house; without explanation – other than saying that she would be back very soon to collect him – she had rushed off. When she left she was almost running: she had been in a lather of anger and urgency. She had left him for *her* to feed. Then, when it was bloody obvious that *she* was not coming to take him home, back to his *proper home,* like she had promised, stupid Grandma had to put him to bed. And he had not stopped crying since she'd left him here.

I don't think I like him very much she thought soberly – and he's too old to blart like this. "Who'd have kids?" she wondered aloud, making Brian jump in startled surprise at the loud question.

Then she cackled and even more loudly, in mock anguish, she told the world, "No more for me! I'm having no more! At my age I can do without kids."

She addressed her grandson directly, "What happened last night? Why did your mom leave you here? And what was that row later on in the night? Was it your hooligan mates looking you up?" Brian shrugged his slumped shoulders. He had certainly heard the shouting, but he couldn't tell his frightening Grandma who had shouted through the letter box. He couldn't tell her about the fight, or the shed, or how his mom had found him.

He mumbled, "Somebody said mom was shouting."

"She's always bloody shouting." his Gran retorted. "There was no need for any hooligan to tell us *that* through the letter box!"

On his previous evening's walk back to the Harding's cottage Frank had thought very seriously about his predicament. What would happen? He knew that Joe would release Brian later that evening as arranged, and he knew that Brian would hare back to his Mom like a scalded cat. He couldn't imagine him keeping quiet. He would heap it all on to him. He'd tell everything that had happened, and a lot that hadn't. He would have made up a lot as he lay trussed up in the shed. He'd lie of course, as he always did, and his doting Mom would believe his every sacred word.

Anyway, Brian did not have to lie at all to condemn him. It was true that Frank had beaten him. He had been roughed up by the evacuees. They had tied him up.

Frank Bourne was dead!

It was at that point in his walk that Frank irrevocably confirmed his big decision: he was running away. He had run out of thinking time and he was running away – tonight. He arrived at the cottage; he had committed himself just in time.

Only he had left it too late: Mrs Harding was waiting at the door to welcome him. There was no escape now; the bath was inescapable.

"Where the hell have you been?" she asked, as she attempted to cuff his ducking head. Her first attempt to hit him had been a feint, and he fell for it. She easily connected with her second swipe.

Without waiting for an answer to her first question, and foregoing the satisfaction she merited after hurting Frank, she asked, "Have you seen our Brian?" Dumbly he shook his ringing head.

"Well everybody else is done. So get your clothes off and get in that bath. Brian will just have to get in after you. He won't like that, but it's his fault if he can't get here on time."

The large zinc-plated bungalow bath stood where it always stood on Saturday bath day. It was in place in front of the fire; waiting for him: a menacing accessory to his murder.

The usual preliminaries were exercised: the unpleasant scrubbing of his body and the painful battering of his head with the rock hard bar of yellow soap. "Stand up!" … "Sit down!" It was very difficult for him to think only of his plan as the punishing routine progressed, but he forced himself to concentrate on one thing alone: timing.

With repetition Edna Harding had lost the advantage of surprise and Frank was able to gauge the moment precisely. He had deliberated on this so much. He closed his eyes – and he took his well exercised deep breath – at the exactly right moment in time!

He had planned to relax as he was immersed: the time of terror when his head would be held implacably under the grey water. But his body betrayed him and he became, and remained rigid. As he had planned it though, he did not struggle as he usually did through these awful traumatic moments.

Amazingly he *was* able to hold his breath. He was in charge of the event; frightened but confident and without the *paralysing* fear of the previous water tortures. His thinking was clear as he controlled his breathing: resisting the urge to expel from his distended lungs, retaining the air, and finally – when he could no longer avoid it – gradually releasing the pressure within his chest.

His month of determined exercising had paid off. When he was released at last; when he was able to gasp life back into his lungs, he savoured the victory.

He had won! He had won again; he had won twice in one thrilling day! Mrs Harding looked hard at him, then without speaking she looked away, throwing the usual sodden towel at him. Subdued she walked to the door and through it into the yard, peering around in the dusk searching for her son.

Frank was still damp but he was dressed when she came back into the kitchen. He was standing with the bucket, ready for his next chore, ready to empty the bath. He looked enquiringly at her.

"Leave it!" she snarled. She called up the stairs to her husband, "I'm going to find our Brian. He knew it was bath day. I'll kill him!" There was no reply: Bill chose to be snoozing. He often did after his bath. Mrs Harding stormed out of the cottage angrily slamming the door.

Emily, who had been waiting for the opportunity, came downstairs and confronted Frank. "Well! You're still alive!" she said happily. "You held your breath – all the time? Did Mom say anything? What's up with her now? And why has she gone out? Where's our Brian?"

At first Frank merely shrugged as she bombarded him with her questions, but she would not be deflected by silent shrugs; he decided that he had to confide in her.

He told her in whispers about the day: about Brian trapping him at the lock, and about the fight. He even mentioned that his two best friends had happened along, and were able to watch as he was knocking the stuffing out of Brian.

Emily listened with rapt attention as she heard how her awful pain of a brother had got what was coming to him. "And you have left him tied up at that shed," she echoed in amazement. "Could he die do you think?"

Frank was not sure that he was reassuring her when he said that there was no chance he would die, but he explained that Joe would be letting him go any minute now. Saying this reminded him that he had to get moving straightaway on his own plan. He could not wait for the inevitable retribution that would come when Brian returned home; he had to run away now.

"You have been really great Emily … I'm going to miss you.

But, I've got to get away … right away … and right now," and he murmured softly. "I love you. … But I must leave now. You know your Mom will kill me when she sees Brian, and he tells her everything. And while he's been tied up he's had time to make up a hundred and more stories and lies."

Emily dreamily asked, "Do you Frank?" He looked astonished until she went on, "You said you love me. *Do* you love me?"

He nervously responded, "Course I do." Then he added, very quietly and self-consciously, "My Love." Following this comment he had to struggle to free himself for she grabbed him. She hugged him. He was the first great Love of her life.

Finally, and reluctantly, Frank was released and Emily watched as he crept quietly up the stairs to collect his things, careful not to disturb her dad. It took very little time. Altogether his belongings comprised a pathetically small bundle of clothes that he clutched under an arm.

Returning to the kitchen, and under the dreamy gaze and close presence of Emily, he took the shopping basket from its place in the pantry cupboard and hastily grabbed a few things from the pantry shelves. He stuffed these with his clothes in the basket.

Emily happily in love wanted more romance. She told him lovingly that she was going with him – wherever he was going! He told her that it would be dangerous; he would be hunted; he had to travel on his own so that he could go quickly.

"I can run faster than you," Emily stated in annoyance, falling out of love for an instant; but then she accepted the inevitable: the need to stay behind, here with her Dad. With a hard pressed mouth to mouth, teeth to teeth, goodbye kiss, and a promise to come back when the war was over, Frank was out of the door and running.

Running away, into the fast thickening dusk.

Chapter 35

Escaping from his past years Frank headed up the canal, running very quickly on the towpath. There was no need to skulk up behind the hedgerow – there was never anyone to avoid on the canal bank at this time of the day.

Although Mrs Harding was abroad searching for her son, Frank felt sure that she would be calling at his friends' and at his Gran's. She would have looked up and down the canal but she knew this was not one of Brian's usual haunts. He would not be meeting her here.

Arriving at the shed once again in this busy day, Frank was surprised and a little startled to find it empty. Joe had obviously done his job and released Brian, but a little earlier than planned. So there had been no need at all for Frank to come back here, he could have made a straight break away – towards Home.

There again, though, he really *had* to make sure that Brian was OK. But where was he? He had not passed him on the way from the cottage to the shed! Panic re-entered his thinking. He walked across to the lock gate thinking to get a better vantage point there.

He stood on the plank footway that was fitted across the lock gate, the same place where he had tried to catch fish. So very long ago it seemed. He was about to leave intending to go on the bridge for a better view down both directions of the canal, when Mrs Harding appeared from nowhere, at the canal side.

She came from the direction of the shed, and she moved swiftly to within a few paces of where Frank was balanced on the narrow foot board across the canal. He was shocked rigid by her sudden appearance. She spoke, and all was made clear to the astonished, fearful, and stranded boy.

"You little bastard," the apparition growled. "I am going to kill you. I'm going to hurt you first, and then I'm going to kill you."

He was trapped: eerily trapped, exactly as he had been earlier in the day by the son of this monster. Frank was trying to think – but he found that his brain had had enough for this one day. It shut down, and he could only stare at the maddened woman.

She continued her menacing growl, voicing terrible threats at the shivering paralysed youngster. Standing, very alone and completely helpless he knew that these were not idle threats: she meant everything that she said. She meant to kill him. All that he could do was wait for her to get him; hit him, hurt him and kill him.

"My son's told me everything." She spoke, in a voice dropped to an almost normal pitch. In this unnatural but conversational tone she continued. "I *knew* ... *I just knew* where to go to find my boy ... And I was right ... I found him lying in that fucking shed. Where you left him – you little bastard! He could have died. But I found him!" Her voice was back in that shriek that raised the hairs on the back of his neck. "He's at his gran's now. I knew that you'd have to come back here so you could torture him some more, so I took my poor lad to my mom's – then I came back here – to have you just to myself – to take care of you! He'll be warmed up now and his Gran will have fed him ... and she'll look after the poor lad until I fetch him and get him home in a minute... the poor love. Getting mobbed and beaten up by *you*! You and your gang of bullying arsehole thugs."

She was getting more and more worked up, and there was no easing of her screeching venom. "You Brummagem bastards are the scum of the earth. How dare they drop you Birmingham shit in our village? And tomorrow I will sort out your mates. I know who they are ... and they'll be sorted."

Reverting to an almost conversational voice she said, in an attempt to gentle persuade, "Come here Frank Bourne!"

Getting no response or reaction from the petrified youth she suddenly screamed at him, "You filthy gypsies from the festering slums of Birmingham bringing your lice and your diseases into the whole county. You're a plague! You brought a bleeding epidemic here … and *you* … you filthy animal, brought those scabies into *my* home. There isn't a cleaner house in the village and you brought that shame on to me!"

There was no point in reminding her that Brian had had scabies and had been scratching his skin, and picking at his scabs quite a long time before Frank developed the disease. Her irrational accusation though had an almost immediate effect on the mesmerised Frank. He was still scared, but angry now to be reminded, so unjustly of those itches and scabs that he had suffered those several months ago. He remembered being told that it was caused by evil bugs burrowing under his skin. Sister Alice, from the far side of the room in the cottage, had told him that and, before she had rushed away, she had given him a whole rosary penance for catching the disease. He remembered having to live with the knowledge and the awareness of invisible evil bugs burrowing through his flesh!

This accusation, being spat at him by Mrs Harding, instantly brought back the pain, the shame, and the fear that he had been forced to carry through the scrubbings and the quarantine. And recollection of that painful and shameful time shocked him wide awake.

She was looking with an evil intensity at the silent white faced boy, but she failed to see the change in him. In the evening gloom her malevolent glare did not appreciate that Frank was no longer the apprehensive boy who, only a minute earlier had been rigid with fear, and desperately hanging on to the guard rail. He was standing upright now, his body was braced. He was erect, poised, waiting – trying to think with a clear purpose: how to get out of this nightmare.

He was not however entirely prepared for her next move. This was not long in coming, but first she changed her tone and tried to cajole him. "I know you've got sense Frank. You know you've got nowhere to go. Come off that plank. Come over here and let's talk about it!"

Instantly she saw that that approach was a waste of time. It was then that she saw her basket, sitting where Frank had placed it by the side of the lock.

"You thieving little Bastard," she cried. "After all I have given you – after all that I've done for you. This is what you do!" She picked up the basket and saw in it the items from her pantry, and his sad 'other' pair of shorts and 'other' pair of socks.

"Are you thinking on going away?" she roared, and in the unreasoning grip of her anger she launched herself at him. With one hand still clutching the basket, the other reached out to capture him, and her outstretched grabbing hand almost reached the boy. To make up the distance she lunged onto the narrow footway.

Almost immediately she was betrayed by the failure of her right foot. This snagged on a jumbled ball of fishing line. The line was held trapped; immoveable on the wooden plank. The fish hook at the lines end had wedged into the gap behind the narrow foot way. Earlier that day Frank had been unable to free it.

Pulled up short she involuntarily – but too late – released her hold on the basket. This splashed into the lock. Her arms flailed, both of them unencumbered now. Her hands desperately sought something – anything – to hold on to.

Frank watched with keen but passive interest as Mrs Harding, with a high pitched scream, fell into the lock. He left the insecurity of the foot board, carefully avoiding the tangled fishing line. He noted with interest that the basket was bobbed clear by the great splash that Edna Harding made when she entered the water. He saw that it had remained floating the right way up.

The fall she made was not an enormous drop. Barges passing through late in the evening always closed the gates at both ends to conserve water. The last boat of the day had passed through some time ago. The gates had been closed for the night: the lock was full. This had limited her fall to less than four feet.

Surfacing she lashed around her at the water, and flailed senselessly at the air. It was getting appreciably darker by the minute. In the light of a half-moon in the clear night she could not see him clearly but she sensed that Frank was above her on the dock side.

She screamed for help then screamed again, "Get me out of here! Get me out of here. Now, you little fuck pig!"

Her frantic efforts achieved nothing other than to hasten her next submersion below the grey black and very cold water inside the seventy foot long lock.

"*Frank. Frank!*" she yelled, searching for the shape of him in the gloom, "Lean over and pull me out! I ain't a good swimmer Frank. I can't swim … you've got to pull me out NOW!" And she spluttered, "And bleeding quick you little arsehole!"

It should have been obvious, even to the single minded woman blinded by panic, and at the mercy of her survival instincts alone, that Frank was not of a size that could reach her, even if he leaned over the lock side. And if he *could* reach her he had neither the strength to hoist her, nor the weight that would allow her to pull herself out.

Finally realising this she screamed another order, "Get a rope … or a stick … Quick." She remembered a long thin tree branch that lay by the shed. She had tripped over it when she arrived. It stood waiting to go onto a fire that had been started there.

"There's a piece of wood by the shed … Go and get that!" she screamed, and spluttered. "For God's sake be quick Frank!" She couldn't see him leaving. She couldn't see anything – other than the greasy flush brick walls, and the water of her prison.

Frank knew which wood she meant. He had debated with Joe how to break it up so that it could be used on the fire. The drowning and now silent woman took some comfort in his return, but then she was dismayed to see the shape of him, with the thin branch, go across the lock and away from her.

She was croaking now, "Give me the end ... For God's sake boy ... give me the end of that wood to hold to ... just to hold on to! Or throw it in then, it'll float, it'll help me float ..."

Frank appeared not to hear her. He continued to the opposite lock-end seemingly oblivious to her despairing scream, *"Give me the end! Give me the fucking end!"*

Well away from Mrs Harding Frank lowered the thin branch into the water. She thrashed desperately in an ineffective attempt to reach it, but she couldn't swim and her thrashing became increasingly feeble. She was fatigued by her efforts to keep afloat and desperately continued with the only thing she *could* do: scraping her finger nails in pathetic attempts to wedge a hold in the slime of the unforgiving walls. Despairingly she saw Frank trying to hook the wood through the handle of her floating basket. His priority was to save the basket.

Mrs Harding was helpless to do anything other than fight to hold on to that greasy black wall. She had only badly damaged hands and bloody finger nails to fight the filthy wall. Strength was leaving her.

Frank removed the wood from the water and pulled open a split at the branches end. At last he succeeded in hooking this under the handle of the basket, and finally he was able to hoist the precious thing clear of the water and on to the lock side. He had been totally preoccupied with his project.

Mrs Harding peered with faint hope as Frank moved across the lock. He stood directly over her. "I had to get my clothes out didn't I?" he said, talking to himself, and noting with obvious satisfaction, "That's something else I've done well today." He went on, but now he was talking to a terrified and silent woman, who was trying to plaster herself against the wall below him.

"I've got some bread, and a bit of cheese in the basket, and ... Do you know what ... I've got that blue bag of currants that you kept in the bottom of the sideboard. I found that bag ages and ages ago and when I was really hungry, I mean *really* hungry, I used to have one, and sometimes I had two of them. I was really scared that you would find out: really scared! But there was still some left, and they're in the basket now." And he said reassuringly, "They'll dry out. And the bread'll soon dry out, and my trousers, an' all."

Something occurred to him, and he continued in the same matter of fact voice, not appearing to hear the woman's piteous almost inaudible cry of 'help me' when he spoke her name.

"Do you know Mrs Harding I poohed in my trousers once. I couldn't help it. I wasn't well you know and I couldn't stop it, my belly was sick. But you didn't notice Mrs Harding 'cos I used Harry's knife and I cut out that other bit: you know that other bit of cloth inside the trousers by your bum. That was the bit covered in Pooh, and you didn't notice. I nearly poohed again when I got home and I was waiting for you to notice it. But you didn't notice."

He rambled on, "Eh, did Brian tell you how I whacked him today Mrs Harding? Oh I did batter him. He won't get me again you know. He's scared now. Anyway I'm going away. Did you know this cut goes all the way to Birmingham?" he asked conversationally.

Mrs Harding sighed down the wall and under the water again. Frank lowered the branch into the loch, and as her head slowly bobbed to the surface he held the branch-end in the air above the woman's head.

There was no hope in the branch. He used it as a pointer.

He remarked casually, "You've got to get rid of all those nits in that head of yours Mrs Harding! We can't have nits you know." His lecture ended, "We can't have nits taken into the house!"

He left the lock side then, and he took the thin branch with him. He replaced this tidily behind the shed, and then, returning to the lock side, he picked up the precious basket.

Without looking around; without a glance into the silent lock, and without a thought to the past, Frank set off down the towpath.

The Evacuee knew where Birmingham lay: he marched in that direction.

He had not been greatly delayed by his instinctive, unplanned detour to Granny Harding's cottage. He fearlessly hammered at the door of the darkened, fast asleep house. There was no response; he lifted the flap in the door and shouted through the letter box, "Mrs Harding's in the Lock!"

He turned away but hesitated, and then felt compelled to return. He hammered once more on the door, and again he bellowed through the letter box. "Mrs Harding's in the lock. She's shouting!" There was no obvious reaction from within the cottage.

This time, when he turned away, he walked to re-join the canal towpath, and there he resumed his trek. Unhurriedly, but with set purpose, he headed along the canal towards Alrewas.

Towards Alrewas; Fradley; the Swan pub; the Coventry canal; Fazeley; the Birmingham canal; the Navigation pub; the Cuckoo pub; the King Edward pub; Lichfield road, and home. The route – etched in his being – became his marching song.

The boy was returning from his war. Without fear he ate four of his precious currants. The Evacuee was going Home.